JUNIOR COLLEGE DISTRICT
of St. Louis-St. Louis County
LIBRARY

5545 West Park
St. Louis, Missouri 63105

PRINTED IN U.S.A.

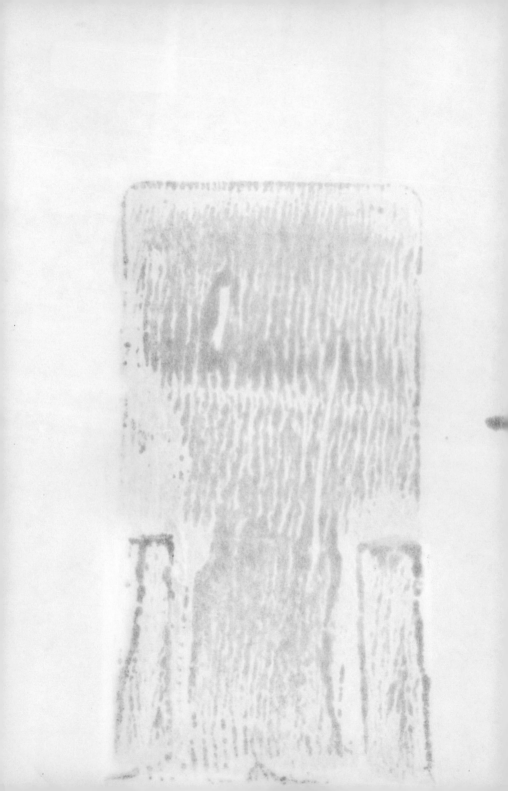

Macmillan Career Book

ENGINEER

Ingenious Contriver of the
Instruments of Civilization

CAREER BOOK SERIES
Under Editorship of Charles W. Cole

ENGINEER, by S. C. Hollister
SOCIAL WORKER, by Margaret Williamson
CAREER DIPLOMAT, by Willard L. Beaulac
SCIENTIST, by Dr. Robert S. Morison
MINISTER, by John B. Coburn
PROFESSOR, by Fred B. Millett
LAWYER, by Talbot Smith
PHYSICIAN, by Dr. Dana W. Atchley
ARCHITECT, by Robert W. McLaughlin
NURSE, by Edith Patton Lewis
JOURNALIST, by Herbet Brucker

ENGINEER

*Ingenious Contriver of the
Instruments of Civilization*

by S. C. HOLLISTER

*The Macmillan Company, New York
Collier-Macmillan Limited, London*

FIRST PRINTING

The Macmillan Company, New York
Collier-Macmillan Canada Ltd., Toronto, Ontario

Library of Congress Catalog Card Number: 66-20211

Printed in the United States of America

Contents

Foreword

This is an especially important volume in the Macmillan series of Career Books. Most young people have a fairly clear notion of what a physician does, or a journalist, or a professor. They may even have a certain sense as to the functions of a lawyer, though Perry Mason and various television district attorneys probably color their ideas in an unduly dramatic fashion. But relatively few young men have more than the haziest conception of the nature and the demands of the profession of engineering. A good many, therefore, go to engineering school only to discover after a year or two that they do not have the appropriate interests and aptitudes. Even more, perhaps, do not choose engineering as a career despite being well suited to it and despite the urgent need for more engineers in this and in all other countries.

But engineering is only a special case of a general problem. During the past three decades I have talked to hundreds of young men and women about their career plans and their career decisions. I am sure that it is an accurate generalization that such plans and such decisions have become much more difficult to reach today than they were in the past. In part, the increasing difficulty arises from the obvious fact of the rapidly growing complexity of our society. There are literally hundreds of new callings, professions, and vocations: atomic scientist, x-ray therapist, city manager, psychiatric social worker, computer operator, parking-lot attendant, skiing instructor, television repairman, airline traffic manager, and hundreds of others—all literally unheard of thirty or forty years ago. Some old callings have disappeared. At the turn of the century every village had a blacksmith. Now it is hard to find one. At the same time many ancient professions have become more complicated, subdivided, and specialized. No longer does a young man merely decide to be a physician. He usually has to choose eventually among psychiatry, surgery, pathology, ophthalmology, pediatrics, cardiology, and a dozen other specialties. And as Dean Hollister points out so clearly, there are many different types of engineer—some relatively old like the civil engineer, some very new like the nuclear engineer.

It has become harder to choose among careers today partly because, for many of them, not only is a college education required but also some training after the four-year college course. Many engineers take one or two years of graduate work beyond the bachelor's degree before beginning to practice their profession. Increasingly, young men who are planning to enter business go for one or two years to a graduate school of business administration, or perhaps substitute for that advanced work in accounting or economics. High school teachers used normally to have just a B.A. or a B.S. degree. Now most of them have a master's degree and some have gone on to take the doctorate. Today, many girls who are going into nursing take five or

even six or seven years in one combination or another of
college and nursing school. To some extent it is an indication of the affluence of our society that so many young people can spend so many years in preparation for their life
work. But even more, the extension of education arises from
the needs and requirements of the most technically complicated society the world has ever seen.

Still another factor that increases the difficulty of vocational choice is the growing tendency toward self-analysis
among students. Heirs to some decades of spreading information and misinformation about psychiatry; victims of
hundreds of mental tests, projective tests, and aptitude
tests; beneficiaries of a deepening concern in school and at
home about problems of "adjustment," young men and
women sometimes hesitate long and painfully before reach-
ing a conclusion about their abilities, motives, and goals.

Many parents do not appreciate the increasing difficulty
of making a career choice. Some of them have confessed to
me that they were truly concerned because their sons had
not made a firm vocational decision by the sophomore year
in college. The concern is understandable, but it is ill-
founded, for, in general and with some limits, the later a
young man arrives at such a decision, the less likely he is to
make a mistake. And a mistake may lead to a real waste of
time, effort, and money.

Considering the problems in connection with career
choices that all young men and women are facing, and real-
izing that what they needed most to help them was truly
authentic information about the various professions and vocations, it seemed evident to me that a series like this one
would be most useful. Discussion with a number of edu-
cators and guidance counselors confirmed the idea and the

Macmillan Company welcomed it as an opportunity to be of real service to young people in secondary school and college. The plan for the series as it has developed calls for a limited number of books on the most important callings. Each is written by a person who has actually practiced and is intimately acquainted with the vocation in question, and who has achieved notable distinction in it. Each is designed to present in a thoroughly factual manner the problems of entrance into and practice of the different professions. But the volumes do more than that, we hope, for they are intended to give a vivid picture of what it is like to be a lawyer, or a professor, or an engineer, or an architect. They endeavor, moreover, to convey a sense of the personal requirements, the rewards and the sacrifices involved in the various vocations. There is no attempt to romanticize the professions or to color them. What these books are designed to do is to help young people in the most practical possible way on one of the two most difficult decisions of life (the other being marriage).

By the breadth and great distinction of his professional career, Dean Hollister is peculiarly qualified to write *Engineer*. He took his bachelor's and his civil engineering degrees at the University of Wisconsin. After varied work in the field of engineering, he became director of the School of Civil Engineering at Cornell University. Then, after a year as associate dean of Cornell's College of Engineering, he was its dean for twenty-two years (1937–1959). He has been a consultant, an adviser, and a committee, board, and commission member on such varied matters as the penstocks of Boulder Dam, the specifications for concrete, reinforced brick masonry, water resources, industrial development, professional development, and isthmian canal studies. As member or officer of a dozen professional associations he has received numerous medals and honorary degrees and is past president of the American Society of Engineering Education.

Thus for many years Dean Hollister has been in intimate touch with the profession of engineering, with leading engineers, with engineering education, and with engineering students. The new civil engineering building at Cornell is named after him—Hollister Hall.

CHARLES W. COLE

Amherst, Massachusetts
1966

ENGINEER

Ingenious Contriver of the
Instruments of Civilization

1

Introduction

There is a tremendous sweep to engineering. Its leading edge is continually cutting into the unknown, undeveloped, and untried. The great middle area is busy with developing and building, with operating, managing, and maintaining not just separate devices but whole systems as well. The trailing edge is busy with the improvement and conversion of outmoded apparatus and operations, to make them again useful, economical, and safe.

Engineering is not a static profession. It is continually changing, continually growing, as mankind's needs and knowledge grow and change. It is incessantly probing the unknown and the untried for new methods and improved results. Its procession of innovations have their impact on man's whole way of life; on his ease of movement, on the range of instant communication, on the health, wealth, and happiness of the people.

Engineering is adventure. It is the story of great bridges, of superhighways, of astronauts in orbit, of seeing and hearing halfway around the world, and of finding new means to use the resources of nature for the benefit of mankind.

The engineer is creative. He is constantly concerned with employing existing scientific knowledge in the service of his fellow men. At the same time, he stimulates research by his demand for further scientific data that he can use in the realization of his dreams. He is not concerned with routine activities but rather with design, contrivance, and innovation. He begins with an idea, a mental conception. He conducts studies and, when necessary, research into the feasibility of this idea. He directs the building and operation of what he has planned.

The engineer does much more. His task is not alone that of contrivance with material things, for which he must possess an extensive working knowledge of scientific principles and facts. He must also thoroughly understand the functions to be performed by the projected work when it is completed, the methods of its manufacture and construction, and the economics that govern its use. He must have an understanding of the crafts that are to be used and of the organization of the work. It is his responsibility to coordinate and guide the contributions of labor, machines, money, and ideas, and to exert the control necessary to attain his objectives within the prescribed limits of time, cost, and safety. Gradually, he brings meaning and tangibility to his initial concept. At the end he has the great thrill of seeing his vision become reality.

This book is intended to give a brief review of the profession of engineering, its history, its present-day significance, its promise for the future. We shall discuss the engineer's contributions toward improvement in man's way of living and toward the growth of the economies of nations, both in the past and in the modern world. The education required for such professional work will be discussed in the light of a rapidly shifting scene in which new demands are constantly being made upon the engineer. We shall then look ahead to the challenges that await those who have the fortitude to embark upon such arduous and exacting labors, those who value above all else the successful pursuit of difficult goals, those whose achievements will contribute to the progress of their times. Engineering makes great demands upon a man; it offers him great rewards.

2

Engineering Works of the Ancients

There is no better way, I think, to grasp the significance of the engineer's function in our society than to trace the contributions that he and his works have made over the centuries through which our civilization has developed. As we review the story, it will become apparent that mankind could not have achieved the state of living we enjoy today without the ingenious facilities contributed by engineers from ancient to modern times.

The engineer's forefather was known in ancient times as the "builder." He combined the functions now performed by the architect, the military engineer, and the civil engineer. He designed and built temples, aqueducts, irrigation systems, municipal water supplies, fortresses, and harbors. Only a few examples of these early engineering works remain to us; but from them we have some evidence of the tools used by these ancient builders and the methods they employed. Their dependence on manpower and their primitive facilities reflected the general practice of forcing war prisoners into slavery as well as their small concern for the worker. We shall see how this attitude changed with the passing of time and how, with increasing capabilities, the builders progressively employed machines, instead of people, expanded commerce and communications, and thereby enriched the nations and their cultures. We begin with what remains from ancient Egypt.

The first builder whose name we know was Imhotep, who was "chief of works" to King Zoser. He built the stepped pyramid at Sakkara near Memphis, Egypt, about 2980 B.C. The pyramid was about 350 by 400 feet at the base and about 200 feet high. The pyramid was made of limestone blocks that were quarried and dressed by hand with copper or bronze chisels, transported by boat from the upper Nile, and presumably hauled up inclines on rollers. Only manpower was used; there was no hoisting or tractive machinery and only the level was used for placing heavy stones. This pyramid was built about seventy years before the Great Pyramid.

In a tomb at Abydos it was recorded that about 2500 B.C., Uni, "superintendent of the irrigated lands of the king," was directed to construct a canal to allow boats to pass the first cataract of the Nile. There is no evidence that at that time they knew anything about building locks. King Necho is said to have caused a canal to be built between the Nile and the Red Sea in about 600 B.C.

At Ur in Mesopotamia there are the remains of a ziggurat, a temple built in the form of a terraced pyramid by the Sumerians, about 2500 B.C. It was about 70 feet high, built of sun-dried brick and faced with fired brick and stone.

The Code of Hammurabi, King of Babylonia (2100 B.C.), records for the first time the legal penalties for poor

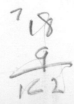

construction. Thus, if the son of the builder's neighbor was killed through failure of the builder's construction, the builder's son should be put to death. Penalties equal to the value of the damaged property were meted out for failure of the work. This is clear recognition of the public responsibility of the engineer, and thus shows that his calling was recognized as a profession over four thousand years ago.

Clay tablets record land surveys in Mesopotamia, using an astrolabe (a graduated circle with pointer for measuring angles to stars) for measuring horizontal angles; and it was there that the measurement of angles and of time in sixtieth parts was begun.

After the reign of Hammurabi, political power gradually shifted from Babylonia to Assyria in the north. There King Sennacherib had a water supply system built for the city of Nineveh in which water was taken from a stream 100 miles away and transferred to the River Kosr, which flowed through Nineveh. As a part of this system, in 691 B.C., he had an aqueduct constructed at Jerwan, with a channel carrying a stream of water 5 feet deep and nearly 60 feet wide across a valley and over a river 20 feet below. The ruins of this aqueduct are sufficiently intact to show that its six arches of 15-foot span were corbeled, or false arches. The corbeled arch is made by increasing the overhang from each side until the two sides join overhead. The true arch, however, carries the load above it downward and outward, tending to thrust the two abutments apart. It is interesting that the Assyrians used corbeled arches, since examples of true arches with "ring-stones" were built at Tell Asmar in Babylonia by the Akkadians before 2000 B.C. True arches were commonly used later in Roman and Byzantine construction.

From 2500 to 1400 B.C., the Minoans lived in Crete. Their principal city was Cnossus. Upon excavation the palace at Cnossus revealed a household sanitation system of a kind that was not known in Europe for another three thousand years. The Minoans had bathrooms with tubs and toilets that could be flushed with water; they used tapered terra cotta pipes not greatly different from those we use today. They collected rain water and conserved its purity by use of cataracts and exposure to the sun. Like most insular people, the Minoans were seafarers. They maintained active commerce with the Egyptians and perhaps with Asia Minor.

The Bronze Age appears to have originated in the Near East about 4000 B.C. This culture spread to the Peloponnesus (probably from Crete, possibly about 1600 B.C.), where bronze was used for tools by some of the native peoples, among them the Mycenaeans.

Mycenae was a city high in the mountains of the Peloponnesus. From here Agamemnon went to the Trojan War. The Treasury at Mycenae, built before 1300 B.C., has a large corbeled arch over a doorway. It was built at least six centuries before those in the aqueduct at Jerwan. The Mycenaeans built bridges with corbeled arches, they also built subterranean vaults and rooms with corbeled, cone-shaped roofs.

The Greek builders did not introduce any particularly new principles of construction, but instead brought an unsurpassed quality of artistry to their structures. They contributed the concept of laying out cities in rectangular patterns of streets and buildings. Aristotle considered Hippodamus the first to plan streets and buildings in a unified scheme. Hippodamus reconstructed Piraeus, the port of

Athens, about 450 B.C., and laid out the Macedonian city
Olynthus, which also has a rectangular plan.

Dinocrates was a great architect-engineer whom Alexander the Great commissioned to lay out the city of Alexandria (about 322 B.C.) at the mouth of the Nile. The
lighthouse on the island of Pharos, harbor of Alexandria,
was built later (about 280 B.C.), by Sostratus. The historian
Josephus said that its light of burning pitch could be seen
from 35 miles at sea, but this is doubtful unless the effect of
cloud reflection is included.

The Greeks built a water supply for the ancient city of
Pergamum (now Bergama) in western Asia Minor about
200 B.C. In three 7-inch tile pipes laid together, they
brought water a distance of 35 miles to a reservoir 100 feet
above the city and two miles distant from it. A 10-inch
pipe ran across a valley and connected this reservoir with
the city. This pipe passed through holes in blocks of stone
that were apparently located at the pipe joints. Because of
the depth of the valley, there were places on this line
where pressures of 300 pounds per square inch were developed. The pipe is gone, and we do not know the material
of which it was made.

The first architect-engineer to write a textbook for his
apprentices was Pytheos, who lived in the fourth century
B.C. His writings are lost, but some of the contents have
reached us through the Roman writer Vitruvius, who
practiced architecture in the reign of Augustus.

Around 300 B.C., the first science of the classical world
began to take form. Euclid wrote his famous geometry
(*geometry* means measurement of the earth) about that
time in Alexandria. Archimedes, about a hundred years
later, working in the Greek city of Syracuse on the island

of Sicily, developed the law of floating bodies and is credited with formulating the principles of the lever, the compound pulley, and the screw.

The Roman Empire extended at one time from Scotland and Germany to the Mediterranean and from Spain to Persia, and remains of their works are to be found over this whole area. Even prior to the Empire, which dated from 29 B.C., Roman engineers had begun the extensive development of the city of Rome. During a period of five hundred years, beginning in the fourth century B.C., eleven aqueducts were built to supply the city, ranging in length from ten to sixty miles. Clemens Herschel, an American hydraulic engineer and translator of the works of Fontana, a sixteenth-century engineer in Rome, has estimated that by the end of the first century A.D., eight of these aqueducts were delivering about 120 gallons per capita per day for a population of nearly two million people. This supply is within 10 percent of that furnished today per capita to modern Rome. There were, however, no sanitary sewers in ancient Rome and human waste was disposed of by cartage. Much of the water was used to flush the streets, to operate the baths and laundries, and to flush the storm sewers.

The Romans were great engineers and they contributed extensively to the development of civil engineering. They not only built the elaborate water supply system for Rome but built systems for cities in France, Spain, Greece, and Byzantium as well. The beautiful aqueducts at Nîmes and Segovia still stand and the latter is still in use. Athens and Istanbul are still served by aqueducts built by the Romans.

The Romans built many roads, the most famous of which were Via Appia, extending from Rome to Brindisi to

the southeast; and Via Flaminia, running north from Rome
to Rimini and Bologna. They built many masonry arch
bridges in conjunction with their elaborate road systems.
They developed the dome; the most noted examples are
those of St. Sophia in Constantinople, now Istanbul, and
that of the Pantheon in Rome. Using a volcanic ash found
on the Bay of Naples, at Pozzuoli, they made mortar that
would harden under water.

The Romans used the Archimedes screw for pumping.
This consists of a pipe coiled up in the form of a helix, or
corkscrew, which is inclined at an angle depending upon
the pitch of the helix. When the bottom end is immersed in
water and the helical coil is rotated about its axis, water
will ride up the coil and be discharged at the top.

The Romans used pulleys, levers, capstans, and counter-
weighted derricks. Their source of power was man's strong
arm and in some cases the treadmill. Their labor force, like
that of all the ancient peoples, was made up largely of prisoners of war held in slavery.

Developments in China seem to have been almost completely independent of those taking place in the Middle
East. The compass, in use in the third century B.C. in
China, was not used in the West until the twelfth century
A.D. The Great Wall of China, by far the largest structure
ever erected, averaging 20 feet in height and about the
same in thickness, was begun in the fifth century B.C. and
eventually extended over 1,700 miles along the northern
border as protection against the marauding nomadic Mon-
gols. It was built by conscript labor.

China lies on the eastern slope of the Asian land mass,
whose drainage is by rivers flowing eastward. The two
largest are the Yellow and Yangtze rivers. For this reason,

trade between northern and southern China was difficult. In 584, the Grand Canal was begun; it connected Peking in the north with Hangchow to the south, and provided over 1,300 miles of waterway. More than a million conscripted laborers worked on its construction. The canal was finished about 610; it was restored by Kublai Khan in 1292. A more direct route, which in places still exists, was built in the fourteenth century. These are the longest canal systems ever built.

The only early Chinese engineer whose name has come down to us is Li Ping, who, in the Ch'in Dynasty (221–207 B.C.), built an elaborate irrigation system in western Szechuan which, after two thousand years, is still in operation. Some principles of hydraulics must surely have been known in his time.

The long caravan trade route overland from the Near East to China was apparently too tenuous a line of communication for sustaining cultural exchanges in any area. The only art that appears to have been brought to the West from China is that of papermaking. In the first century A.D., paper was made from old fish nets. By the eighth century, excellent paper was being made by the Arabs in Samarkand; and in Baghdad there were paper factories operating under Chinese supervision. Gradually papermaking spread to Egypt and on to Italy and France.

Although many of the achievements we have discussed would be noteworthy ones today, they become much greater achievements when we realize that there was little scientific information available to the engineer before the eighteenth century. We shall see as we discuss various fields of engineering that the early works of the engineer were always achieved through the application of a qualitative insight with little or no scientific data or principles for guidance. The engineer was obliged to establish a kind of scientific bridgehead. At some later date, science was developed and was then able to explain in more detail how the achievement actually worked.

The branches of science most used by the engineer today were actually evolved in response to the need for more exact understanding of the principles involved. In the late sixteenth century, Simon Stevin in Holland described how two or more connected strings placed at some angle to the vertical would share the weight of one or more loads. He demonstrated the triangle and parallelogram of forces and he showed what shape a weightless cord would take when fixed at the ends and carrying loads distributed along its length. You will note that these are important practical problems, leading to a later understanding of the suspension bridge.

Regiomontanus (whose real name was Johann Müller), a German astronomer who lived in the mid-fifteenth century, wrote the first book dealing wholly with trigonometry, the measurement of triangles. His book was not published until 1533, fifty-seven years after his death. It deals first with spherical trigonometry, much needed especially by the astronomer, and then with plane trigonometry, needed in land surveying. It contains no equations, however. This development in algebra did not emerge until nearly 100 years later. Regiomontanus' book was neither complete nor was it analytical; indeed, trigonometry was not developed to its present form for another two hundred years.

In 1638, Galileo wrote a book which founded two new sciences; the mechanics of materials, and dynamics. He discussed the proportioning of a beam built into a wall at one end and carrying a load at the other. His method, although in some respects in error, nevertheless made possible the approximate design of such beams; that is, it made possible the proportioning of such a beam in advance of erection, to carry a given load eventually to be placed upon it. This was the first time in man's history that a beam could be proportioned in advance. Galileo's achievement seems the more remarkable when we remember that he had none of the strain gauges or other instruments now used to determine by measurement the principles he sensed from crude experiments.

Galileo also discussed the path of a projectile fired from a cannon. He discussed bodies in linear motion and bodies in free fall. He understood and used the first two laws of motion later ascribed to Newton. Finally, he demonstrated that a projectile in a vacuum would have a trajectory which was a second degree parabola.

In Galileo's day, cannon were made of cast iron or bronze. Gunpowder had been known in Europe for about four hundred years. In 1242, Roger Bacon wrote a formula of $\frac{7}{17}$ saltpeter and $\frac{5}{17}$ each of sulphur and charcoal, and said that ". . . with such a mixture you will produce a bright flash and a thundering noise, if you know the trick." Cannon were being made in Florence in 1326. Gunpowder was not used for blasting, however, until the seventeenth century. Dynamite is a modern explosive invented by Alfred Nobel in 1863.

In the Middle Ages the principal structural achievement was the beautiful Gothic arch with its flying buttresses. These arches were built with only intuitive insight into their action. The Cathedral of Notre Dame in Paris is one of the most notable examples of the use of the flying buttress in support of the arch.

Use of the word *engineer* has been traced back at least to the twelfth century. In Roman days the classical Latin term for military constructor was *architectus militaris;* but in 1196 we find the Latin term *encignerius* used in Lombardy. In 1238 the spelling is modified to *inzegnerium.* In France the designation *maistre engingnierre* was used in 1248, modified in 1276 to the spelling *engegynnyre.* In Germany *ingenieur* appeared before the middle of the fifteenth century; this word is still in use, as it is in France. The origin of our word *engineer* is connected to the German word, and is associated with the word *ingenuity.*

Looking back over man's history prior to about 1600 it is clear that the engineer achieved much in the way of building, and little in the way of machines. He was limited by the materials at hand, which were chiefly wood, stone, and brick. He had little scientific knowledge to help him. Except for crude water wheels, windmills, and sails, he had no mechanical power. The power of a man could be enlarged only by the lever, the pulley, the wheel, the wedge, and the screw. All of the building in the Middle Ages was done with no more facilities than these.

The ancient engineers produced notable works that brought wealth and greatness to their countries. They provided Greece and Rome with security, communication, and health through fortifications, harbors, roads, bridges, and water supply. Without these, the large cities could not have survived. The most notable of their buildings, the temples and churches, became larger and more complex as new structural concepts were developed empirically. The pressure for knowledge was leading toward the emergence of the scientific era. The invention of printing, in the mid-fifteenth century, promoted the dissemination of knowledge and widened the participation of people in the development of new knowledge and in the exchange of ideas.

The accumulation of scientific knowledge from the time of man's emergence until 1600 A.D. amounted to less than that which a modern youth takes with him from high school to college; and yet great structures and public works, mining and refining of metals, and maritime commerce had been developed in support of an expanding wealth and a broadening culture.

3

Civil Engineering
in Modern Times

In 1684, about forty years after Galileo's death, Leibnitz published in Germany his first paper on the differential calculus. His publication opened a floodgate of analyses of all sorts of practical problems which, until the invention of the calculus, could not be solved. Since about 1700, practically all the techniques of quantitative analysis now used in engineering have been developed. Physical experimentation and mathematical analysis ran hand in hand. Usually leading the way were examples of engineering works that engineers had successfully achieved, some through partial analysis, others from tests on large- and small-scale models, but generally with a fine intuitive insight into the actions involved.

Two major consequences arose from the new analyzing capability. The first of these was the founding in France in 1747 of the famous École des Ponts et Chaussées (School of Bridges and Roads), with the great bridge engineer Jean-Rodolphe Perronet as its director. This was the first school of engineering. The Corps des Ingénieurs des Ponts et

Chaussées had already been organized in 1716, following the establishment of the Corps du Génie (Corps of Engineers) in 1672.

The second important consequence was the rapid expansion into new areas and new levels of technology that engineers began to undertake. In France, bridges, roads, and waterways were extensively developed. Perronet's own bridge over the Seine at the Place de la Concorde, finished in 1789, is considered one of the most beautiful masonry-arch bridges in the world. This bridge is notable for its flat arches, obviously the result of a more discriminating analysis of arch action than the earlier bridge builders could make. It should be noted, however, that a full analytical treatment of the arch built with elastic materials was not to be available for another seventy-five years. Clearly Perronet's success was due to his fine intuition, reinforced only by the incomplete method of analysis available to him, and by observations on bridges he had built.

During this active period in France, there was a group of engineers in England who were building canals and lighthouses. James Brindley built 140 miles of canals connecting the industrial Midlands to the sea at Liverpool and to the Severn. This was a tremendous undertaking at that time, involving locks, tunnels, and highway bridges, and an aqueduct over the Dove River with twenty-three arched spans. Such construction stimulated the coal and iron industries and contributed to export trade.

John Smeaton, who was the first to call himself a "civil" engineer, undertook the construction of a masonry lighthouse to replace the old timber Eddystone Light on an exposed rock 14 miles off Plymouth in the English Channel. This was completed in 1759. Smeaton used interlocking stones that he interlocked in turn with the rock foundation. He also used Italian pozzuolano cement found at Pozzuoli, near Naples, which unlike lime would harden under water. It was the forerunner of our modern portland cement, invented in England in 1824 by Joseph Aspdin and given its name because its color resembles that of the limestone found on Portland Isle in the English Channel. Smeaton's Eddystone lighthouse stood for over a hundred years, until it was replaced by a taller masonry structure.

The latter part of the eighteenth century was a period of great development in two other areas. Experiments made in England by Joseph Black and others on combustion and chemical combinations were reinforced and put into an orderly system by Antoine Laurent Lavoisier in France in 1789. Four years earlier, in England, James Watt, after nearly twenty years of labor and $200,000 invested by Matthew Boulton, his partner in the venture, had succeeded in producing the first practical steam engine capable of wide adaptation. Thomas Savery's steam pump, patented in 1698, and Thomas Newcomen's "atmospheric" pumping engine, invented in 1712, were not capable of similar general application. Coal was being mined in Cornwall and iron was being made and worked in the industrial Midlands. Power was needed both to pump out water from the mines and to hoist the coal. It was also needed to operate blowers and rolls in the iron mills. At the time there was little science available to turn to for aid in solving many pressing practical mechanical problems. What scientific discoveries there were came about through tests made to seek such answers. Lavoisier in France was operating the state gunpowder arsenal, and English scientists and engineers were all connected in one way or another with industries. The contributions of Watt, Lavoisier, and others made possible a tremendous thrust forward in the industrial life of Europe, especially England. This thrust also came at the right time to nurture the growing republic just formed across the Atlantic.

England's burgeoning industries created a great need for better transport facilities. Two Scottish engineers, Thomas Telford and John McAdam, developed road building to a practical art with methods more economical in both labor and materials than those used by the Romans. It is said that Telford alone was responsible for over 900 miles of road and about 1,100 bridges in Scotland. McAdam developed a method of road construction still in use and known by the name *macadam*.

Telford used cast iron in many of his arch bridges, including an arched span of 170 feet over the Severn at Tewksbury. His greatest bridge, however, was built over the Menai Strait between the coast of northwest Wales and Anglesey Island. This was a suspension bridge supported by chains of bars of wrought iron linked together at their ends, to form a central span of 570 feet. When Telford commenced building this suspension bridge in 1819, he had no scientific theories to guide him, and many engineers of that day claimed that chains of wrought-iron eye bars would not support themselves in a 570-foot span with a sag of 43 feet, let alone a roadway with vehicles. Telford constructed a full-scale, eye-bar span, and measured the pull with a weigh-beam. Then he hung weights on the chain to simulate the roadway with its load. In this way he determined the sizes required for the chain. He built a large testing machine and loaded each member to one and a half times its required capacity in the bridge. Thus the engineer built safely in advance of theory.

When the French heard of the English work on suspension bridges, they sent Louis Marie Henri Navier from the government's École des Ponts et Chaussées to study the matter. He published the first approximate analysis of stresses in the suspension cable in 1823.

Stresses in modern suspension bridges, such as the Golden Gate Bridge, designed by Joseph B. Strauss and built in 1937, or the Verrazano-Narrows Bridge, designed by O. H. Ammann and completed in 1964, may now be analyzed in advance by more accurate mathematical methods based on Navier's original work. Although analysis is available today, many matters of major importance still remain in which the engineer must rely upon his own judgment: the foundations, the form of towers, the roadway structure, traffic accommodation, selection of materials, and the "details" of structural design and construction procedures. Remembering always that "a chain is no stronger than its weakest link," the engineer must have a searching eye for that weakest link.

Telford was instrumental in the organization of the Institution of Civil Engineers in 1818 and he became its first president. This was the first such organization devoted to the furtherance of professional knowledge and accomplishment in engineering. The American Society of Civil Engineers, formed in 1852, was the first such society in the United States. Today it has a membership of more than 50,000 civil engineers.

The rapid expansion of industry in Britain and the need for mass transport of goods in the United States opened a new opportunity for the application of the steam engine. In Durham, England, George Stephenson built the first steam railroad in the world, running from Stockton to Darlington, a distance of 25 miles. In 1826, the first train, carrying

600 passengers, was hauled by a steam locomotive, also of Stephenson's design, at a speed of 12 miles an hour. Although the line was intended for freight, a passenger service soon developed.

The canals from the Midlands to Liverpool enjoyed a profitable monopoly, but transportation was slow. There was great resistance on the part of the canal owners to the superior competition that the railroads could furnish with their higher speed. However, technical problems relating to the shape and material of the rails and their spacing, of track construction, and of rolling stock, had to be resolved immediately to accommodate such speed. Iron rails supported on wood ties were introduced. In 1829, Stephenson developed his "Rocket" locomotive, capable of 35 miles an hour. In 1830, the line from Manchester to Liverpool was opened, and by 1850, about 5,000 miles of railroad had been constructed in Great Britain. A superior form of transport was firmly established.

Meanwhile, in America, the Erie Canal was built from Albany to Buffalo and opened in 1825. The chief engineer was Benjamin Wright, who later built the Delaware and Hudson Canal. Among his junior engineers was David Thomas, who later became the engineer on the old Welland Ship Canal between Lake Erie and Lake Ontario, in Canada.

The traffic up the Mohawk Valley on the Erie Canal spurred the people in Philadelphia and Baltimore to attempt development of a rival trade route from those cities to the Ohio Valley and then west. Among the engineers engaged on this enterprise were a number of West Point graduates. Although a canal was undertaken in Pennsylvania, from Reading to the Susquehanna River, and the Chesapeake and

Ohio Canal was following westward along the Potomac, the mountainous area farther west made canal building difficult and expensive. The progress of railroad operations in England turned the attention of American engineers to that mode of transport.

The Baltimore & Ohio Railroad was chartered in 1827. Charles Carroll of Carrollton, one of the signers of the Declaration of Independence, laid the first stone in July, 1828. Six years later the railroad had reached eighty-two miles to Harpers Ferry; two more years saw another branch completed to Washington. The chief engineer of these early sections was Jonathan Knight, who had gone to England to study the railroad work going on there. It was 1853 before the rails reached the Ohio River at Wheeling, West Virginia. Many of the forms and methods of construction needed for the great railroad development in America were worked out on this first road.

Two short railroads, the Mohawk & Hudson (between Albany and Schenectady) and the Schenectady & Saratoga, were built in the early 1830s. It was on these railroads that the famous locomotives, the *DeWitt Clinton* made in New York and the *Robert Fulton* of British construction, were operated. During this time also, Horatio Allen built the South Carolina Railroad, 136 miles long. An American locomotive called the *Best Friend* was operated over this line in 1830.

In 1835 a company was incorporated to build the Erie Railroad from Hoboken, New Jersey, across the southern tier of New York state counties. It reached Dunkirk, on Lake Erie, a distance of 483 miles, in 1851. In 1869, the Central Pacific, building eastward from California, met the Union Pacific, building west from Omaha, at Promontory

Point on Great Salt Lake, thus establishing a railroad 1,775 miles long and connecting the Pacific Coast by rail and river to the Eastern Seaboard. These roads were followed rapidly by the Northern Pacific, the Southern Pacific, and the Santa Fe. Fifty years after the beginning of railroading in this country, there were four transcontinental lines opening the West for the great American expansion.

The construction of canals and railroads during the eighteenth and early nineteenth centuries created a new kind of problem—that of embankment stability against sliding. Failures sometimes took place when clays and silts were present. The first helpful book about this problem was *Landslides in Clay*, by Alexandre Collin, published in France in 1846. Charles Coulomb, at the time a military engineer on the French island of Martinique, had published a paper in Paris in 1773, which for the first time dealt successfully with the stability of retaining walls. These two authors defined the field of soil mechanics, the basis of foundation engineering, geological engineering, and soils engineering.

The extension of the railroad would not have been possible without a rapid development of bridge engineering. Stone arches were not feasible; in remote places they were both too slow and too costly to construct and material was frequently unavailable. On the other hand, timber was accessible and wrought iron bolts and rods could easily be transported. Trusses therefore evolved. Timber-trussed arches had been built earlier for highway use. The most notable of these were Lewis Wernwag's 340-foot covered-arch bridge at the Falls of the Schuylkill in Philadelphia, and Theodore Burr's 360-foot span over the Susquehanna at McCall's Ferry. The McCall's Ferry Bridge (1815) was carried away by ice shortly after completion. The Philadelphia Bridge, built in 1812, burned in 1838.

The new railroad trusses were not arched but possessed parallel chords. Leonardo da Vinci's *Codex* contains a drawing of a wooden bridge of this kind (*c.* 1483), but there is no record that it was ever built. Palladio's *Architecture* (1570) contains a design of such a bridge, which he built with a span of 100 feet; but for some reason trussed bridges did not gain acceptance. It fell to a group of American bridge engineers—Howe, Town, Whipple, Bollman, and Pratt—to develop the truss for practical use. In 1840, William Howe built one of his wooden bridges over the Connecticut River at Springfield, Massachusetts, which had seven spans of about one hundred ninety feet each.

It is interesting to note that the method of analysis of trusses was not established until seven years later, when in 1847 Squire Whipple, an instrument maker of Utica, New York, published a small book on the subject. His method of analysis was not refined to the degree now believed necessary, but his book did make possible the proportioning of the members of the bridge in an adequate way. Whipple became one of the leading bridge engineers of that period.

The broader rivers have been major barriers to land transportation. Some of these have been spanned by notable bridges built for both highway and railway transport. We have already discussed Telford's suspension bridge of 1826 over Menai Strait. In 1849, Robert Stephenson, George Stephenson's son, undertook a railway crossing nearby. He finally decided upon a tubular bridge consisting of cellular flanges above and below, with two vertical webs made of wrought-iron sheets riveted together. This produced a tunnel-like box through which trains could run.

William Fairbairn conducted experiments for Stephenson on scale models of tubes of various shapes from which they arrived at the proportions for the tubes. The structure consists of four spans; the two nearest shore are 230 feet long, and the two channel spans are 460 feet long. These are essentially what are now called plate girders, with common flanges, thus forming a box section. They were fabricated on barges along the shore, towed into position between the piers, and hoisted more than 100 feet into final position by hydraulic jacks. Adjacent spans were attached over the piers to produce a continuous girder. This bridge, the Britannia, is still in service and is among the longest spans for plate girders ever built. This is another case of empirical design. The ability to analyze the buckling strength of such a structure came many years later, in the present century.

About this same time, Colonel Charles Ellet, a graduate of École Polytechnique, built a suspension bridge that had a span of 1,010 feet over the Ohio River at Wheeling, West Virginia, using cables formed of parallel wires. The bridge lacked a stiffening truss and was in service only three years before it was wrecked by wind. It was repaired by German-born John August Roebling, a graduate of the Polytechnical Institute in Berlin.

A suspension bridge was built by Roebling over the Niagara Gorge in 1852–1855. It had two decks, the upper carrying a railroad and the lower one a highway, and its span was 822 feet. Roebling used hold-down cables to prevent vibration in the wind. Even though stiffening trusses extended between the two decks, the structure proved to be too flexible for railroads and after forty years of service was replaced by a steel arch.

Immediately after building the Niagara Bridge, Roebling constructed a suspension bridge across the Ohio River at Cincinnati with a span of 1,000 feet. He used inclined as well as vertical suspenders to prevent wind damage since hold-down cables could not be used. This bridge is still in service.

Roebling's most famous bridge is the Brooklyn Bridge, which was completed in 1883. It has a span of 1,595 feet and a clear height above the East River of 133 feet. Here again, as in all his other bridges, Roebling used main cables with parallel steel wires. The Brooklyn Bridge had been in service nearly thirty years before a mathematical method of analysis of its action was devised.

Meanwhile, in 1868, Samuel C. Keefer, a Canadian engineer, built a suspension bridge across the Niagara River near its mouth. This bridge had a span of 1,260 feet. It did not have hold-down cables or inclined suspenders. It was wrecked by the wind after twenty years of service.

Suspension bridges of tremendous size have been built in the twentieth century. The most notable examples are the George Washington Bridge in New York, with a span of 3,500 feet; the Golden Gate Bridge in San Francisco, 4,200 feet; and the Verrazano Bridge over the Narrows, in New York Harbor, with a central span of 4,260 feet and twelve lanes of traffic. A bridge under design in England will cross the Humber at Hull with a span of 4,580 feet, or nearly seven-eighths of a mile. It will carry eight lanes of traffic.

One of America's most distinguished bridge engineers was George S. Morison, who graduated from Harvard in an arts course in 1863 and from the Harvard Law School in 1866. But, after being admitted to the New York bar, Morison found legal practice distasteful and turned to engineering. He had shown considerable interest in and talents for mathematics, surveying, and architecture while in college. After some years as assistant to other engineers, he entered practice on his own. During his career he built many bridges, including sixteen large ones—one over the Ohio, five over the Mississippi, and ten over the Missouri. Today it would be almost impossible to go from an arts course into bridge engineering because of the technical advances since Morison's time; and there is, in these times, little opportunity to study in an engineering office. In that day, however, there were no schools in America in which bridge engineering was taught.

Two noted British engineers of this period were Sir John Fowler and his associate, Sir Benjamin Baker. Fowler had served as a consultant to the government of Egypt, where he constructed extensive irrigation works, organized the railroads, and reconstructed many factories. Baker had engaged in bridge construction and was also chiefly responsible for the underground tube system in London. He was also in charge of the final stage of construction of the first Assuan (Aswan) Dam.

In 1882, Fowler and Baker were engaged to design and build a railroad bridge over the Firth of Forth near Edinburgh. They decided upon a cantilever bridge with two main spans of 1,710 feet each as the stiffest and most wind-resistant type of structure. They also used steel for the first time in major bridge construction; 58,000 tons of steel were used, all made by the open-hearth process, a new method in those days. Another innovation of their bridge was the use of hydraulic riveting machines. For a generation this bridge contained the longest spans in the world. It is still in service.

In Elizabethan times, the great city of London had a population of almost 150,000 people, but it still drew its water supply chiefly from wells. In 1582 a water wheel was installed between two piers of London Bridge. This wheel was turned by the ebb and flow of the tide, and the power produced pumped water from the river into the city through lead pipes. The use of river water, however, caused much disease in London.

In 1609 a more adequate supply from Hertfordshire was provided by an open ditch forty miles long. This was a private venture and paid off handsomely. Eight similar companies were organized during the eighteenth and early nineteenth centuries, drawing water mostly from the upper Thames. In 1902, the water supply of London was coordinated under the Metropolitan Water Board.

In the eighteenth and nineteenth centuries the water supply of Paris was undergoing a similar evolution. The city began to take water from the Seine by pumps. Paris also had a large storm sewer system that collected water from buildings and streets and emptied it into the Seine. No domestic sewage was permitted in this system. Sewage was collected in cesspools which, from time to time, had to be cleaned out and the excrement hauled away. The cholera epidemics of the first half of the nineteenth century brought both London and Paris to a realization of the need for comprehensive systems of sanitation. In Paris, separate systems for storm and domestic sewage were adopted, while in London they were combined.

In the United States there were only four cities with a population of over 10,000 in 1790. At that time there was only one municipally owned water system. In 1896 there were nearly 3,200 water systems and 40 percent of these were publicly owned.

New York City brought water by tunnel from the Croton Reservoir in 1842. A new reservoir was added in 1907 with the construction of the new Croton Dam. In 1892 a twenty-one-mile line of 4-foot steel pipe was brought into the city of Newark. In 1867, Ellis S. Chesbrough, who had been consultant to the Department of Public Works in New York, built an underwater tunnel extending far out into Lake Michigan as a water supply for Chicago.

While American engineers were bringing fresh water to cities from outlying streams, a number of European cities had been developing filtration works for water purification. After Robert Koch discovered the water-borne typhoid bacillus in 1882, filtration was relied upon to remove bacteria. After 1900 it was supplemented by chlorination.

At the turn of the century, Baltimore, New Orleans, and six other American cities with populations of 20,000 or more were without sewers. Nevertheless, of the 1,524 cities with a population of 3,000 or more, 97 percent had water supplies and 70 percent had sewers.

In the twentieth century there have been great achievements in civil engineering works. They have been made possible in part by the development of steam and mechanical equipment and in part by electric power. A few examples of notable works will indicate the nature of these accomplishments. The first of these great works was the Panama Canal, which was built in the decade between 1904 and 1914. While the Suez Canal was finished in 1869, it was initially a small ditch, built chiefly through sand with a maximum cut 60 feet deep. Its original construction required the removal of a million cubic yards of earth with little or no rock. (Subsequent widening over the years required the removal of an additional 5 million cubic yards.) At Panama, however, 270 million cubic yards of earth and rock had to be removed, and three sets of double lock-chambers 1,000 feet long, 110 feet wide, and 42 feet deep were built to lift ships to Gatun Lake 85 feet above the Atlantic Ocean; and a similar set of locks was built to lower them to the Pacific.

London's "Underground" had stirred much talk of a subway in New York, but it was not until 1900 that any construction was undertaken. The first contract called for eighteen and a half miles of two- and four-track construction. Since then, many times that amount of subway work has been done in New York alone. Similar subway construction has been done in Boston, Philadelphia, and Chicago.

In 1905 the Hudson and Manhattan Railway tubes were completed under the Hudson River with Sir Benjamin Baker and three other British specialists from the London Underground in consultation. An American engineer, Clifford M. Holland, built the first vehicular tunnel under the Hudson in 1927. In the meantime, the Pennsylvania Railroad had constructed its tunnels and terminal in 1909. Other tunnels have since been built under the Hudson and East Rivers for both vehicular and rail traffic. In 1910 a tunnel was built under the Detroit River by digging a trench in the river bottom and lowering into it sections of tube which, when joined together, formed the tunnel. Tunnels at Baltimore and Norfolk were built in this manner.

Civil engineering now embraces a series of specializations, all having to do with public works. They include bridge engineering, sanitary engineering, highway engineering, railway engineering, transportation engineering, water supply engineering, hydroelectric engineering, structural engineering, and construction engineering. Some of these specializations overlap with others; for instance, structural engineering deals with buildings, bridges, dams, and other structures. Nevertheless, some engineers specialize in the more restricted fields while others engage in a broader range of work. Although transportation engineering overlaps specific forms of transportation such as highways and railways, it deals with the coordination of all traffic by all methods of transport rather than exclusively with the detailed engineering of any single form. Civil engineering also includes the specialized field of regional planning, necessary for proper urban development and proper land and water use.

While civil engineering embraces many specialties, the civil engineer needs to understand the general fundamentals of all of them even though he may specialize in only one or a few branches. One should become a "generalist" in civil engineering before becoming a "specialist" in a single aspect of the field.

Civil engineers need to be well grounded in a wide variety of subjects, including structural geology, materials of construction, hydrology, fluid mechanics, mechanics of materials, and soil mechanics. In addition, they must understand electrical theory including circuits and electronics; heat engineering including thermodynamics and combustion; and steam, internal combustion, and reaction engines. They should also have a general course in biology in preparation for work in water supply and sanitation. All their work must be founded on a strong preparation in mathematics, physics, and chemistry.

In the mid-twentieth century the civil engineering profession is facing its mightiest challenges. In West Pakistan a dam will be built to control the Indus River and make possible the development of power and the irrigation of a large area of arid land. It will be the largest dam ever built and will cost $800 million, financed mainly by the United States government.

A tunnel under the English Channel has been proposed at a cost of $400 million. This will connect the center of London with the center of Paris by a direct rail line that, including the limousine rides at each end, can be traveled in about the same time now required by air.

On the North American continent an adequate water supply is becoming a critical matter in some areas. It is expected that the United States will double its population in another forty-five years. In the meantime, there is a big shift of population to the Southeast and especially to the Southwest. The southwestern states are already short of water. The northeastern states are experiencing water shortages both in the great metropolitan areas and in smaller communities.

A number of schemes are being discussed to alleviate the water shortage. The most comprehensive of these would connect the Yukon River in Alaska, through a series of reservoirs, with northwestern Mexico and with the Great Lakes area. At the same time waters from rivers emptying into Hudson Bay would be diverted to flow into the Great Lakes. Water from the Great Lakes would in turn be distributed to the Middle Atlantic states and to metropolitan areas within these states. The preliminary estimate of the cost of this vast scheme is of the order of $100 billion.

In California, work is being done on a plan to redistribute water at a cost of about one billion dollars.

The expected rise in population also points up the necessity of recasting our transportation system. The interstate highway system is only partly finished. When completed, it will have cost some $50 billion. Most passenger and freight transportation needs reorganization and commuter service to cities is breaking down in some areas. In fifty years we will have three times the urban population that we now have; and fifty years is a relatively short time in which to reorganize mass transport in the urban areas. It is conceivable that from $20 to $30 billion will have to be spent in recasting the mass transportation system in the United States.

The number of urban communities has greatly increased and industry has expanded extensively. Both discharge wastes into the same waters needed for processing or for domestic use. Many industries use large amounts of water for cooling and in the process return much warmer water to the streams. The country faces an enormous problem of cleaning up the extensive bacterial, chemical, and thermal pollution in our streams and lakes. In some places such pollution is already a hazard to health as well as a deterrent to fish and other aquatic life.

It is easy to see that the water and transportation problems form only a part of the enormous expansion of public and private works that the civil engineering profession will be engaged in over the next two or three generations.

4

Mining, Metallurgical, and Petroleum Engineering

The working of metals has been a preoccupation of man from the earliest times. Primitive man had only wood, bone, baked clay, or stone from which to make his artifacts. Civilization could not advance without more sophisticated tools than were possible with these materials; the development of metals was therefore necessary to progress. In fact, the successive early periods of the cultural advance of man have been named in accordance with his growing knowledge of materials; hence the Stone Age, the Bronze Age, and the Iron Age.

The names Bronze Age and Iron Age are used chiefly by the archaeologists who invented them to mark the ages of the artifacts found in their excavations. They cannot be clearly separated. Iron is subject to corrosion to a greater degree than bronze and few iron tools survived. An iron tool dating from about 3700 B.C. was found in the Pyramid of Kephron in Egypt and Egyptian records dated about 3500 B.C. refer to iron.

Acquaintance with metals could have come about only by accidental discovery. A few metals occur in some places in a substantially pure state. Others reveal themselves in the presence of fire. Copper, tin, lead, and zinc could be found in either of these ways. All are useful metals in the development of tools. The Egyptians used copper tools and some say they knew a method of tempering or alloying copper to produce a hard cutting edge; but no tools so hardened have been found and the knowledge of such a process, if it existed, has been lost. The art of mixing copper and tin to form bronze, a harder material than copper, is also very old; its use in Egypt dates from 4700 or 3800 B.C., depending on the authority. Herbert Hoover believed that the stone-cutting of the Egyptians was done with iron tools which have been corroded out of existence. The Bronze Age in Asia Minor spanned the period from about 4000 to 2000 B.C. It is known that the Phoenicians were transporting tin from Spain and Britain about 1500 to 1000 B.C.

Other metals frequently found in a relatively pure native state are the so-called precious metals; the earliest known of these are gold and silver. Silver was often found associated with gold but the method used to separate them by the ancient metal worker is not certain. They were used for ornaments and eventually replaced bone, seashells, and copper or bronze coins as the primary material for monetary exchange. These metals then became the symbol of wealth, both of men and of kingdoms.

The next group of important metals is the one that made possible the development of machines. While copper, tin, lead, and zinc are all important industrial metals, by far the most important are iron and steel. Along with the development of these metals came the necessary development of progressively better fuels with which to melt and refine them.

It is not known for certain where or when steel was first made. The bellows was used about 1500 B.C. to force the refining flame to a higher heat. In Homer's time (tenth century B.C.) tempering and hardening of steel was a well-developed art. In medieval history the expressions "Damascus blade" and "Toledo blade" are used to designate a superior steel for swords made in Damascus and Toledo. It is known that at that time charcoal was used in the manufacture of such steels.

The most comprehensive of the earliest books on mining and metallurgy, *De Re Metallica*, was written in 1530 by Agricola. The author was a Bavarian who wrote in Latin and invented Latin technical terms as he went along. As a result, his book was practically undecipherable by later readers. It was finally translated into English in 1912 by Mr. and Mrs. Herbert Hoover. Mr. Hoover, later to become the thirty-first President of the United States, was at the time only thirty-eight years old and was already an internationally famous mining engineer. His historical notes to this translation are valuable.

Other metals and metallic compounds were produced at an early period. Soda was mined and used before 3500 B.C., and so was bitumen. Mercury was mined and refined prior to the Christian era; and alum, antimony, zinc oxide, red-lead, litharge and sulphur are also of early origin.

Coal was barely known to the ancients, who depended on wood from which they could make charcoal. The mining of soft coal in Britain after the twelfth century introduced new fuel for both domestic and industrial use. Its domestic use had become so widespread by the sixteenth century that Queen Elizabeth barred the use of coal in London because the smoke and soot created such a nuisance. She also barred deforestation in certain areas where the trees were being cut down for making charcoal. Abraham Darby, an English ironmaster, began using coal to smelt iron in 1709. By 1745 the second Abraham Darby had found a way to make coke from coal and to use it in smelting. This new process gave great impetus to the iron industry as well as to coal mining. The coal production in the United Kingdom was about two and one-half million tons in 1700 and increased fourfold during the eighteenth century.

The engineering aspects of the processing of wrought and cast iron for industrial uses were developed mainly in England, and by the eighteenth century many machines made of these materials were in operation. The quality of iron was not standardized and therefore it was necessary to designate the products of special mills for special uses of iron.

Before 1854 Henry Bessemer in England had invented a long projectile for cannon that would rotate about its long axis while in flight. No one was interested because this heavy projectile would require a gun made out of material much stronger than the cast iron then in use. Bessemer therefore set about developing a process to make steel, and two years later, in 1856, he had achieved his converter, in which he blew air through the molten metal to reduce the carbon content of the iron. The process was difficult to control; moreover, most of the ores were high in phosphorus. Sidney Gilchrist Thomas, a clerk in an East Side police court in London, learned in an evening course in chemistry that if anyone could solve this problem, he would make a fortune. He and a cousin, Percy Gilchrist, who was a metallurgist, joined forces and in 1878 Thomas patented his modification of Bessemer's process. He lined the con-

verter with lime bricks instead of the silica bricks used by
Bessemer, thus changing from an acid to an alkaline process.
The first practical application of the process was made at
Cleveland, England, in 1879.

At the time Bessemer was developing his converter, William Siemens, a German-born Englishman, the son of a
prominent industrial family, was working on the regenera-
tive open-hearth process which he patented in 1861. In this
process, hot air is passed through the molten metal to oxi-
dize the carbon present. The hot waste gases are used to
heat alternately either of two brick checkerwork chambers
through which the incoming air is passed and preheated.
This conservation of heat greatly improved the efficiency
of the process.

The Martin brothers in France introduced scrap iron
into the Siemens furnace along with the pig iron. Most steel
today is made by this Siemens–Martin process.

The molten metal used in the processes discussed above is
molten pig iron, which contains from 4 to 5 percent carbon. The purpose of blowing air through the metal is to reduce the carbon content by oxidation. Steel has a range of
0.01 to 0.9 percent carbon. The more carbon there is in the
steel, the harder the steel. Carbon content of cast iron is
above 1.7 percent and it is brittle material of much lower
tensile strength than steel.

Small additions of other metals often have profound
effects upon steel. Such alloys have formed a large and important family of special steels. Nickel manganese, vana-
dium, cobalt, molybdenum, chromium, and tungsten,
added singly or in combination, are important metals in
producing steels for special uses. Some of these metals in
very small amounts impart important properties as catalytic

agents. Some of them, such as tungsten, chromium, and nickel have important uses in themselves.

Pittsburgh was becoming an iron center in the United States as early as 1810 because of the coal found in western Pennsylvania. Before that time, small mines along the seaboard had produced the coal and iron that were needed. Later, iron from a few small local mines together with some iron brought in from Missouri fed the young industry. The Gogebic Iron Range on the Northern Peninsula of Michigan became active in 1881. In 1890, the great deposit of iron ore in the Mesabi Range, seventy miles north of Duluth, was discovered. Iron ore began to move through the Great Lakes to Pittsburgh with the help of a canal at Sault Ste. Marie built by the Fairbanks–Morse interests of Vermont. Coke, needed for melting this iron ore, was produced from coal from the nearby mines in Pennsylvania and West Virginia. Pittsburgh became the center of the steel industry. By the Second World War, the United States alone was producing about half the world's output of steel.

The development of the iron and steel industry in the United States came in good time to support the rising industrialization of the country. We have already noted two important British developments that contributed in a major way to the steel industry, the Bessemer–Thomas process of making steel patented in 1878, and the Siemens open-hearth process patented in 1861, and modified by the Martins. These are the principal methods by which steel is made today.

Since the Second World War a new method of making steel has been developed in Austria. In this new basic oxygen method, oxygen instead of air is blown into the molten

metal in a Bessemer converter. Better control of the oxidiz-
ing process and greater efficiency are claimed for the
method, and it is gaining acceptance. Installations have
been in operation in Europe and Japan and more recently
in the United States.

A brief discussion of a problem involved in this new
process will illustrate the work of an engineer. The Bessemer converter is a large pitcher-shaped vessel mounted on a
horizontal axis, it may hold 300 tons of molten iron at
above 2,200°F. Jets of air are introduced under pressure
through openings in the bottom and pass upward through
the molten metal. The oxidation of carbon and other im-
purities causes the temperature to rise to the approximate
level of 3,000°F, maintaining the resulting steel in a
molten state. The lining of refractory material can
endure temperatures only a little higher than that of the
molten steel. When pure oxygen under pressure, instead of
air, is blown through the bottom openings, the heat produced by the more rapid combustion erodes the openings.
The oxygen is therefore introduced from the top through a
water-jacketed "lance," causing the jet to play upon the
molten pool. The need for more rapid action through in-
troducing the oxygen into the vessel was determined by a
rationalization based on chemistry and metallurgy; but what
this rationalizing does not spell out is the choice of process
and of materials to achieve the desired end. This must be
achieved by the ingenuity of the engineer acting with all
the information he has at his command. He cannot devise a
design by computation alone.

A young country can get ahead only in the event that it
can produce wealth. Agriculture, forest products, minerals,
and power are needed for a balanced and expanding econ-

omy. The United States had all of these from the beginning. It was not, however, until the California gold rush of 1849 that mineral production on a broad scale was begun.

French explorers found outcrops of lead ore in Missouri in 1715. Later, lead was found in the more complex ores of Utah, Idaho, and Colorado. Nevada and Idaho have produced a great quantity of silver and gold, and Idaho has produced much lead. Montana and Arizona have produced copper, gold, and silver. Arizona produced $150,000,000 worth of metal from a single mine, and $500,000,000 was taken out of California, all during the latter half of the nineteenth century. The mineral contribution from the West was a stimulus to the growing nation and the great westward migration.

One of the most abundant metals on the earth is aluminum, one of the constituents of common clays. It is not found in the metallic state. In 1827, in Germany, it was refined for the first time, but no economical way was found to reduce any practical quantity by chemical means. In 1855, an electrolytic process was discovered in France; but since batteries were the only source of current at that time, no practical use could be made of it. Not until 1886 was the first feasible scheme devised. This was achieved by Charles M. Hall, who began this work while he was a student at Oberlin College, with the encouragement of his chemistry instructor.

Hall's process, which is in use commercially today, consists of electrolizing purified aluminum oxide dissolved in molten cryolite, in a steel cell with a carbon lining. The lining serves as the cathode and a carbon anode dips into the molten bath. Five to six volts at 50,000 to 100,000 amperes are supplied to the cell.

Aluminum, a strong metal of light weight, has been used

in many places, but the development of aircraft could not have progressed without it. In sheet form, and with appropriate alloys, it has the strength of steel and weighs less than half as much. At present it is produced from bauxite, an oxide of aluminum, and over two million tons are produced annually in the United States. No way has yet been found for producing the metal commercially from clays.

Magnesium is another lightweight metal used chiefly in cast form. It is "mined" from sea water. (To some degree, sea water contains all the metals in solution.) Magnesium, when ignited, burns with a brilliant white light. It must be machined with care.

Uranium, for a long time called a "useless" metal, is now mined extensively for use as a nuclear fuel. Its use as a source of energy for electric power production is increasing.

In recent years a number of rare metals, heretofore chiefly of academic interest, have been under development. There is considerable possibility that new alloys made with these rare metals will produce materials with properties beyond the range now available. If this is the case, and many believe it is, such new alloys will develop machinery and equipment for new processes.

Some early mining engineers in this country studied at the École des Mines in Paris or at Freiberg in Germany. The first American school was founded in 1864 at Columbia College. Seven years later, the American Institute of Mining and Metallurgical Engineers (now the American Institute of Mining, Metallurgical and Petroleum Engineers) was organized. Today it has about forty thousand members.

In the twentieth century the function of the mining engineer has grown progressively, quite apart from the function of the metallurgical engineer. The mining engineer locates and explores the extent of mineral deposits, plans the kind of workings suitable to the ore body, and is responsible for the construction and operation of the mining facilities. He must be well versed in geology, mineralogy, and petrography; and, of course, he must be well grounded in mathematics, chemistry, and physics. Instead of locating an ore body by "prospecting," with pick, shovel, and pan, the practice from time immemorial until very recently, he now uses magnetometers, scintillometers, Geiger counters, core drills, seismic equipment, and other such geophysical instruments as may be appropriate to the minerals involved. He must also know mining equipment and methods, and he may need to know process metallurgy and ore dressing.

Allied to the mining engineering field is the specialized field of petroleum engineering. The function of the petroleum engineer is the extraction of crude petroleum and natural gas from the earth. He is in charge of locating and drilling the well and of its subsequent operation. Locating and mapping the extent of a petroleum deposit are done by a geophysical engineer working in conjunction with geologists and paleontologists. The refining of petroleum is the concern of the chemical engineer.

Metallurgy is a fine example of the need for a combination of physical knowledge and a knowledge of the art of manufacturing and processing. It has been known for centuries that pure iron heated in the presence of charcoal becomes steel. It has also long been known that steel after heating, depending upon the rate and the environment in which it is cooled or chilled, takes on different properties (and that the crystalline structure is altered). The temperature boundaries for different cooling procedures are well established. Why these things happen as they do is still a mystery to science. In the meantime, the metallurgical engineer gets on with his business of preparing metals for various uses, and the structural and mechanical engineers select and use the metals appropriate to their machines, structures, and processes. This situation will probably continue for many years before the preparation and refining of metals is reduced to a wholly scientific exercise.

The metallurgist is concerned both with the extraction of the metal from the ore and with the processing and utilization of the metal after extraction. Like all engineers, he must be well grounded in mathematics, physics, and chemistry. He must know the atomic and crystalline structure of metals, as well as solid state physics. He must be especially well versed in physical metallurgy, including alloying and heat treating of metals. To all this he must add a thorough knowledge of the processes of hot and cold working of metals, of casting, rolling, forging. He must also be well grounded in fabricating methods such as welding and machining, and understand the effects on metals of stress and of chemical and physical environments.

A new field for the metallurgical engineer has to do with the blending of metals with ceramics to produce materials able to withstand high temperature. This is a complex field but one which, it is expected, will yield large rewards.

5

Mechanical Engineering

The simple mechanical tools such as the hammer, the chisel, and the awl were in themselves considerable achievements. They involved the application of materials as well as the manner of use, and they date from earliest man, separating him from his ancestral primates who had not the mental power to contrive. The processes employed by skilled artisans are based upon these simple tools.

The next step from tools to mechanical devices that multiply man's effort, was an achievement of a higher order. The simple roller, the inclined plane, the wedge, and the lever were used by the ancients before the Christian era. Indeed, they had carried these devices one step further by developing from the roller into the wheel, followed by the chariot and the cart; and by developing the inclined plane into the screw, since the screw is simply an inclined plane wrapped around a circular cylinder.

Just before the dawn of the Christian era, some of the most distinguished philosophers and mathematicians of the time explained the multiplying power of the lever and the compound pulley. Three Greeks, Ctesibius, Hero, and Archimedes, made some important beginnings in the application of fluids, both by developing devices and by establishing basic principles of action. We have already mentioned Archimedes' screw pump for lifting water. He also explained the principle of buoyancy. Ctesibius and Hero developed the piston force-pump. This involved the use of a flap or poppet valve that was already in use in Egypt. For some time the Egyptians had used a pump consisting of a wheel with earthen buckets fixed on the rim. As one of these buckets entered the water in an inverted position, considerable resistance to filling occurred, until a valve was put in its bottom which could open to let out the air and later close when righted to retain the water.

Hero proposed using a reciprocating piston pump for a fire engine. "Hand pumpers" of Hero's form were used as fire engines in America well into the nineteenth century. Hand fire-fighting apparatus, using the principle of the piston and operating like a large syringe, was used by the Romans and was still in use in 1666 at the Great Fire in London. Hose came into use in the seventeenth century.

Hero invented a simple form of steam turbine. He suspended a hollow sphere on hollow horizontal pivots above a closed cauldron of water under which a fire could be built. He placed two tubular elbows on opposite sides at the equator of the sphere pointing in opposite directions in the plane of the equator. Steam would then pass from the cauldron through the hollow pivots into the sphere and out the elbows, thus causing the sphere to rotate about its axis. This is a simple reaction turbine. There is no record that Hero's engine was ever put to mechanical use. When steam turbines were developed about the beginning of the twentieth century, advantage was taken not only of the reaction but also of the expansion of the moving steam.

If a closed vessel filled with steam is cooled, the steam

will be condensed and a vacuum will be formed in the vessel. A pipe attached to the vessel and extending into a pool of water will cause the vacuum to suck water until the vessel is filled. The reason for the suction is that the weight of the atmosphere presses on the pool and forces the water up the pipe into the vessel.

Since a column of water 32 feet high exerts the same pressure as the atmosphere (at sea level), the suction can lift water only 32 feet. If steam is then let into the vessel after it has been filled with water, and the suction pipe closed, it can drive the water up another pipe to a height dependent upon the steam pressure. In 1698, Thomas Savery built a pump in England based upon this principle. It had no moving parts other than valves which were turned by hand.

Thomas Newcomen, in 1712, replaced the vessel with a large vertical cylinder fitted with a plunger. The steam forced the plunger to the top of the cylinder. When the cylinder was cooled (thus producing a vacuum in it), the atmosphere would force the plunger to the bottom. Newcomen attached the plunger to the end of a horizontal beam pivoted at its center. To the other end of the beam he attached a rod extending down to the plunger of a plunger pump. Thus when the piston in the steam cylinder was forced down by the air, the pump plunger would move up, bringing water with it.

Savery's pump and Newcomen's pumping engine depended upon atmospheric pressure to produce the lifting of the water. They are really atmospheric pumps rather than steam engines. Savery's device, much modified and called a pulsometer, is frequently used today. Newcomen's engine has long been superseded.

James Watt, at that time an instrument maker of Glasgow University, noted the great loss of heat during the alternate heating and cooling of the cylinder of the Newcomen engine. He first used the steam as the driving force on the piston. Then he built a condenser to provide a partial vacuum on the side of the piston opposite the steam. To obtain more uniform motive force, he then arranged valving to cause the steam to act first on one side of the piston and then on the other (double acting). Finally, in 1782, he patented a valve arrangement to cut off the steam supply after a partial stroke, utilizing the expansion of the steam to complete the stroke.

Watt's steam engine was the first to be constructed in a form suitable for uses other than pumping. It was adapted at once to hoisting coal in the mines and to furnishing motive power for the rolls in the iron works and for the looms in the textile mills. In the 1820s, it was adapted to locomotives, making possible the development of the railroad.

What was involved in Watt's development of the steam engine affords a good deal of insight into the interplay between engineering and science. When Watt began his work in 1763, there was only one bit of scientific information applicable to his problem: that of converting steam into mechanical work. This was what is now called Boyle's Law (1662), which states that in a perfect gas at constant temperature, the volume varies inversely as the pressure. Thus, in a cylinder, doubling the pressure on a gas reduces its volume by one-half, if the temperature is held constant. But Watt was dealing with a vapor, not a gas; and the two do not behave quite the same.

Assume that a cylinder containing a piston is connected to a boiler full of steam. When the steam is turned into the cylinder, the piston is driven down the cylinder, the pressure and the temperature of the steam remaining constant. If the stroke is to be repeated, the connection with the boiler must be closed and an exhaust port in the cylinder must be opened so the steam pressure is then reduced to atmospheric pressure. The piston is then moved back with the exhaust port open, and when it reaches the head of the cylinder, the port is closed. The valve admitting steam from the boiler is then opened and the cycle begins again. In this process the only function of the heat imparted to the steam in the boiler is to cause it to build up pressure. This pressure is maintained constant through the depth of the stroke, when it is suddenly discharged to the atmosphere and wasted.

Watt saw that after, say, one-fourth of the stroke was completed, he could cut off the supply of steam and allow the stroke to be completed by the *expansion* of the steam in the cylinder. He noted that at the end of the stroke, the temperature of the steam had dropped materially. This could mean but one thing; that the heat in the steam was being caused to do mechanical work, which was not the case when the inlet valve remained open during the entire stroke. This conclusion suggested another idea—that if instead of exhausting the steam to the atmosphere, the steam in the piston could be exhausted to a vacuum, this would cause a still greater pressure drop and hence the removal of a greater amount of heat could be effected. Watt therefore exhausted the steam into a cooled chamber, which he called a condenser. In this way he utilized the heat in the steam to perform mechanical work.

Watt devised an instrument that would draw a curve of pressure varying with the travel of the piston; he called this curve an indicator diagram and patented it in 1782. The indicator diagram stimulated interest in the study of heat. This eventually led to the law of the expansion of gases with change of temperature by Dalton and Gay-Lussac in 1802, and to the theoretical development of the ideal cycle by Carnot in France in 1842. Laplace and Lavoisier invented the calorimeter in 1780. In 1843, the Englishman Joule reported his measurements on the mechanical value of heat. In 1847, Helmholtz in Germany wrote on the transformation of energy. Thus the science of thermodynamics was founded, spurred by Watt's engineering of the steam engine.

The Institution of Mechanical Engineers was founded in 1847 with George Stephenson as its first president. The American Society of Mechanical Engineers was founded in 1880. It now has a membership of sixty thousand.

The greatest contribution of the steam engine came with its application to manufacturing. In the England of those days, this meant principally the textile mills. With increased use of iron, there was a need for power tools for iron working. Crude machine tools were developed, initiated by Henry Maudslay. The more accurate forms of machine tools that led to mass production were invented in the United States by Eli Whitney, who had invented the cotton gin (a machine for removing seeds from raw cotton) in 1792. By 1800, his ideas for precision tools for machining metals had taken form. His first venture was in the construction of guns. Whitney's goal, however, was to achieve an accuracy that would permit interchangeability of parts in general manufacture. With Whitney's achievement of this goal, the American form of industry, mass production, had its birth.

New England's many streams afforded low-head water power development, ideal for small industrial plants. Immigrants from England brought with them a knowledge of textile machinery. By 1800, textile mills were becoming established, the first in Pawtucket, Rhode Island. James B. Francis, a young engineer from Wales, was brought to Lowell, Massachusetts, by George Washington Whistler, an early railroad builder (and the father of James McNeill Whistler). Francis started hydraulic experiments in Lowell which eventually led to the Francis hydraulic turbine. The steam engine afforded power where water power was not available. The cotton gin in the South had meanwhile boosted cotton production to the point where, in 1845, the United States produced over seven-eights of the world's cotton.

Machine tools made possible the establishment of the Colt Armory at Hartford which produced the famous revolvers of frontier days. Two of the workers there, Francis A. Pratt and Amos Whitney, founded the famous shop for making tools for the manufacture of sewing machines, bicycles, typewriters, and in modern times, airplane engines. From this shop came two other famous machine tool engineers, W. R. Warner and Ambrose Swasey, who established a plant in Cleveland.

In 1804, John Stevens successfully undertook the building in Hoboken, New Jersey, of the first seagoing steamboat, the *Phoenix*. At the same time a steamboat was being developed by Robert Fulton, an artist and draftsman of Philadelphia. Fulton's *Clermont*, with a 20-horsepower engine, made four miles per hour on the Hudson in 1807. Soon afterward steamer service between New York and Albany was established, and the 130-mile one-way trip was accomplished in one day. Stevens invented the screw propeller in 1802.

By 1811, Nicholas Roosevelt had built the *New Orleans* in Pittsburgh and initiated river traffic to New Orleans. It is said that by 1840 there were a thousand boats on the Ohio–Mississippi waterway. In 1818 the first steamboat appeared on the Great Lakes.

In this country, John Ericsson exploited Stevens' development of screw propulsion. Britain, however, was more active in ship construction and became the dominant producer and developer of ocean-going steamships. The Cunard Line began regular service to America in 1840. This line first used screw propulsion on the *China,* which sailed in 1862. It was during the Civil War that the American Navy began its conversion to steam, and its initial venture into using steam alone was the famous Union turreted gunboat, the *Monitor,* which Ericsson built. The large ocean liners used compound reciprocating engines throughout the nineteenth century, achieving 30,000 horsepower on a single vessel.

In the latter half of the nineteenth century, both Charles T. Porter and John E. Sweet independently developed high-speed reciprocating engines in both small and large sizes. These were introduced into all sorts of manufacture.

The large, heavy-duty, low-speed compound engine was of the Corliss type. One of these engines was built by Allis-Chalmers at Milwaukee and was exhibited at the Philadelphia Centennial Exposition in 1876. It stood 30 feet high, had a 10-foot stoke, and developed 1,400 horsepower. The first Corliss compound engine was built in 1875 for the water supply of Easton, Pennsylvania. Large pumping engines were built by Allis-Chalmers for such cities as Chicago and Louisville. As late as 1919, Allis-Chalmers built a pumping engine 85 feet high for Louisville, with a capacity of 30 million gallons a day. In 1910, Philadelphia was using twelve triple-expansion Holly pumping engines with a capacity of 20 million gallons per day each.

The first practical steam turbine was built in 1881 by a Swedish engineer, C. G. P. de Laval. It consisted of a wheel with closely spaced blades projecting from the rim. A set of nozzles caused jets of steam to impinge on these blades from the side. The blades were curved so that the jet of steam was sharply altered in direction. Such a turbine is called an impulse turbine. Using high pressures, de Laval achieved speeds of 40,000 revolutions per minute.

In England at about the same time, Charles A. Parsons was developing a multiple-stage reaction turbine, which consisted of alternate rows of moving and fixed blades, with the moving blades attached to the shaft of the rotor and the fixed blades attached to the casing. The steam would enter the casing at the high pressure end where the blades were small and closely spaced in each row. The movable blades were curved in one direction and the fixed blades curved in the opposite direction. Successive rows of blades increased in diameter and spacing so that as the steam flowed from the high pressure toward the low pressure end, it would expand. This, together with the alternating directions of the flow of steam, produced a reaction in each moving row causing the rotor to turn on its axis. Most steam turbines today are built on this principle. In 1901, a turbine of 2,000 horsepower was installed at Hartford, Connecticut. Turbines have become successively larger; a single machine with a capacity of one million horsepower (750,000 kw) was recently installed in New York City.

The large steam requirement of the engines of the latter half of the nineteenth century necessitated radical improvements in boilers. Earlier boilers were fired with wood, but by 1850 coal began to be used for steam generation. United States production for that year was 8 million tons. Thirty-five years later, 70 million tons were mined, of which about 30 million were used in railway locomotives. By 1920, coal production was up to 590 million tons, of which 135 million were used by the railroads.

The first practical internal combustion engine was produced by Dr. Nikolaus Otto in Germany in 1876, following the analysis and suggested design of a gas engine in 1862 by Beau de Rochas in France. This was a four-cycle engine, similar to the gasoline engines now in general use in cars. Exhaust gas from the blast furnaces in which pig iron is refined from iron ore was discovered to be useful as fuel in 1895. This led, in 1903, to the installation of a 40,000-horsepower plant, using such gas, at the Lackawanna Steel Company in Buffalo, New York. Natural gas from oil wells has also been used in stationary internal combustion engines.

The greatest use of the internal combustion engine, however, was in mobile units such as automobiles. The earliest motor cars were built in Europe. The first reliable car was built by Karl Friedrich Benz in Germany in 1885, and the Duryea brothers of Springfield, Massachusetts, built the first American car in 1892–1893. Henry Ford built his "gas buggy" in 1896, and organized his first company in 1899. The automotive industry has been built up almost entirely in the twentieth century. In 1900, there were 8,000 automobiles in the United States while in 1962, over 92,000,000 vehicles were registered.

The automotive engine was a natural ancestor of the aircraft reciprocating engine. In recent years the jet engine has taken the place of the reciprocating engine for high-speed flight.

The gasoline engine has been joined in the power field by the diesel, invented in Germany by Dr. Rudolph Diesel in 1892. In this engine air is compressed, after which fuel is injected, and ignition is accomplished by the heat of compression. Diesel fuel is cheaper than gasoline, hence the diesel engine has become a popular power unit. Nearly all the locomotives in this country are diesel-electric powered; that is, a diesel drives an electric generator which in turn drives motors on the axles. The over-all efficiency of these locomotives is about four times that of steam locomotives.

With the development of diesel engines and their adoption on the railroads, the demand for coal was greatly reduced, so that by 1960 only about 400 million tons of coal were mined. The major portion of this was used for the production of electrical energy.

Expressed in tons of bituminous coal equivalent, it has been estimated that the total energy production in the United States for the year 1960 breaks down as follows: 23 percent from coal, 42 percent from petroleum, 31 percent from natural gas, and 4 percent from hydroelectric plants. Thus petroleum and natural gas account for nearly three-fourths of the energy produced. This is due to the introduction of the automobile and the diesel engine and the industrial use of natural gas.

In the last century and a half, an industrial revolution has taken place, made possible in large measure by the mechanical engineers. They have revolutionized transport and have powered manufacturing of all kinds. Their prime movers —hydroturbines, steam generators, or internal combustion engines—provide power for central electric stations, for ships, trains, motor cars and aircraft and for all manner of factories. In this country at least, they have multiplied the physical power of each workman about two hundredfold.

In each case, some mechanical device has been developed and put into production long before a completely scientific explanation of its internal function was available. Combustion and lubrication are still under scientific study. The thermodynamic cycle in the steam engine was not available for study until large engines were actually in use. The general pattern has been that investigations were not carried out until there was something to investigate. In no case did a full-blown body of science precede the application of theory to practical devices. But this application was not made through guesswork; where theory was not available, empirical data were gathered to make certain the limiting conditions were safely and adequately met.

The mechanical engineer is concerned with the design, manufacture, and operation of all sorts of mechanical things, and he is concerned with the factories that produce them. He may be interested also in the operation of systems in which the mechanical units are only components. For example, the mechanical engineer is interested in the conversion of heat energy into mechanical energy by converting the latent energy in coal and other fuels into the mechanical energy of a rotating machine. This may be done by burning the fuel to produce steam which in turn drives a turbine; or by burning gaseous fuel in the engine, as in internal combustion and jet engines. The mechanical engineer also converts mechanical energy into heat; and he uses mechanical energy to produce refrigeration. By such processes he can both heat and cool buildings.

The mechanical engineer designs and builds water turbines for hydroelectric plants. He is interested in the strength and manufacture of the moving parts of electrical machines. He is also engaged in the design, manufacture, and installation of pumps of all kinds for all purposes, whether for a city water supply, or for producing and maintaining a high vacuum.

The mechanical engineer is involved in the design and operation of all sorts of manufacturing plants in which mechanical apparatus is utilized. He is involved in all modes of transportation, not only the design and manufacture of the power plants used in the vehicles, but also much of the design of the vehicles themselves, at least their mechanical parts.

The work of the mechanical engineer interlaces that of engineers in other branches. He works with the architect on the mechanical equipment of buildings and with the naval architect in installing the power plant and providing the mechanical equipment of ships. He designs and directs the manufacture of contruction equipment used by the civil engineer and he supplies the mechanical equipment needed in civil engineering works. He designs and constructs the mechanical equipment needed in mines and in the metal-working industry, and he designs and installs mechanical equipment for the chemical industry.

In providing professional services to so wide a range of activities, the mechanical engineer must have special capabilities relating to the mechanical application and use of heat, the mechanical transmission of power, and the design and manufacture of machines that utilize mechanical power. He must have the ability to grasp quickly the significant elements of functions and actions of machines and mechanical systems new to him, and to make the best application of mechanical principles to serve the conditions.

An educational program for the training of a mechanical

engineer should first of all include an understanding of the basic laws of physics, mathematics and chemistry, commonly needed by all engineers. He should, in addition, have thorough training in the properties of materials, and in the design of mechanical parts using various appropriate materials. He should understand the basic principles of combustion and the characteristics of various fuels. He must understand thermodynamics and gasdynamics, and the dynamics of fluids, including aerodynamics and lubrication. He should also have training in nuclear engineering. It is essential for him to understand manufacturing processes including casting, forging, metal cutting, welding, and heat treating. And it is important that he be well grounded in electrical engineering, including the design of electrical machines, electrical circuits, and electronic devices such as computers and their use in control systems.

There is a great opportunity for the mechanical engineer in the discovery of new ways of meeting future requirements. New materials and new sources of power are coming into being. Simplification and redesign made possible by new materials, or a better understanding of the performance of old materials, offer great economic possibilities. Automation, which is the process by which more manufacturing power is put into each worker's hand, frequently calls for the redesign of extensive manufacturing systems. Increasing competition in world markets exerts a continuing pressure toward innovation, improvement, and economies. All these factors contribute challenge, vitality, and opportunity to the field of mechanical engineering.

6

Electrical Engineering

Although electricity is all about us, pervading natural phenomena in many ways, it was evident to the ancients in only three ways. Magnetic rocks, called lodestones, had the power of attracting iron. Amber, when rubbed briskly on a woolen cloth, would attract certain light objects, like pith balls. But most fearful was lightning.

The mariner's compass was the first important instrument that employed electrical forces. It was discovered that when a lodestone was floated on a card on water, it would indicate the general direction to the pole star. Mariners have used the lodestone, or later the compass needle, since about the twelfth century, although the Chinese are said to have used the compass since the third century B.C. The principles of electromagnetism were not discovered until the nineteenth century A.D.

An electrostatic machine that duplicates the frictional effect of rubbing amber bars with wool was invented in Germany by Otto von Guericke in 1663. It consisted of a sphere of sulphur mounted on an axis and turned by hand. If the hands were held against the sphere while it was being rotated, a charge would result, producing a spark. Later refinements consisted of glass cylinders and glass discs against whose surface various materials were made to rub.

In 1745, Pieter van Musschenbroek invented a means of storing charges of static electricity like those generated by rubbing amber. This device, the Leyden jar, was a form of capacitor. Two years later, Benjamin Franklin used it to collect static electricity while flying a kite during an electric storm, conducting the charge received by the kite along the wet string to the jar. From this experiment Franklin devised the lightning rod.

Professor Luigi Galvani at Bologna discovered in 1786 that when he touched a dissected frog's leg with a knife while an electrostatic machine was being operated in the same room, the frog's leg would twitch. He later found that the twitching could be produced by touching the frog leg with a conductor formed of two different metals.

Professor Alessandro Volta at Pavia devised an eletroscope to replace the frog leg in sensing the electrical impulse created when two conductors of different metallic content are brought into contact. From these experiments he was led to the invention of the battery in 1800. For the first time a continuous flow of current was artificially produced.

A Danish professor, Hans Christian Oersted, demonstrated in 1820 that when an electric current was passed through a wire above and parallel to a compass needle, the needle deflected at right angles to the wire. Thus electromagnetism was discovered. In the same year André-Marie Ampère demonstrated that a coil of wire through which a current was passing acted as a magnet without the presence of an iron core, and that two such coils would repel each other as would two magnets. Ampère also distinguished electrical potential (voltage) from the quantity of current flowing (amperage). In 1826, in Germany, George Simon Ohm determined the resistance of a conductor to the flow of an electric current.

Michael Faraday, an English chemist and physicist, showed that when a wire suspended by one end had its free and movable end dipping into mercury in which a permanent magnet was supported, the free end would revolve continuously about the magnet when the wire was connected to one terminal of a battery and the mercury to the other. In 1832, Faraday in England and Joseph Henry in America, working independently, demonstrated the principle of electrical induction and showed that it took place when the current was rising or falling. In 1831, Faraday had discovered that when an electrical conductor was moved sidewise across a magnetic field, a current was produced.

The first practical electrical device using the findings of Oersted, Ampère, and Ohm was the telegraph, which Samuel F. B. Morse demonstrated on a line between Washington and Baltimore in 1844. A rather complex instrument had been tried in England, but since it required four to six lines and involved complicated sending and receiving instruments, it was not deemed practical. Morse's instrument printed the message in dots and dashes on a paper tape. Since the instrument made a clicking noise, it was not long before printing was dispensed with and receiving was done by ear. Much later, high-speed transmission reverted to a more elaborate printing process. In 1856 the Western Union Telegraph Company was founded, with Ezra Cornell, who had built the Washington–Baltimore line, as principal stockholder. (Profits from this company led to the founding of Cornell University in 1865, and Morse's original receiving instrument is now at the university.)

There was still a long way to go, however, before a dynamo or motor could be built. It was not until 1865 that a machine was available that had electromagnetic fields self-excited by the current being generated in the rotating armature. One such machine was built by Henry Wilde in Manchester, England, and another by Moses Farmer of Salem, Massachusetts. In 1871, Zénobe Théophile Gramme, a Belgian, produced a hand-powered machine that had a ring-wound armature. In the following year, Professors George Moler and William A. Anthony of Cornell University built a Gramme machine with a capacity of about 12 horsepower. It was exhibited at the Philadelphia Centennial in 1876 and was subsequently used to furnish street arc-lights through an underground cable on the Cornell campus. This machine is still in working order.

Thomas A. Edison invented the incandescent filament lamp in 1878, using a platinum wire. He decided upon 110 volts with parallel circuits. In 1880, he adopted the carbon filament.

Edison's first application of his lamp system was in 1879 on board the steamer *Jeannette* bound for the Arctic. This system worked well for two years, until the ship was crushed in the ice. He also outfitted the *Columbia* with electric lights in 1880, and furnished each stateroom with a five-candlepower lamp. This ship was built at Chester, Pennsylvania, and was put into regular service by the Oregon Railway and Navigation Company between Portland and San Francisco.

In September, 1879, a small experimental power plant was built in San Francisco by the California Electric Light Company, using three Brush generators and furnishing current for arc lamps. The service proved so popular that within a year a second, larger plant was built. These two plants inaugurated the first regular commercial electric service.

An Edison direct-current station to supply current to 3,000 Edison incandescent lamps was built at Holborn Viaduct, London, in January, 1882. The British Electric Lighting Act of that year, however, outlawed the building of large central stations in order to protect the gas lighting monopoly. In September, 1882, Edison opened his Pearl Street Station in New York. Babcock and Wilcox boilers supplied steam to Porter and Allen engines of about 900 horsepower capacity or enough power to supply about 7,200 lamps.

In 1885, George Westinghouse acquired the American patent rights to the Gaulard–Gibbs alternating current system which had been demonstrated in London four years earlier. He installed the system in Great Barrington, Massachusetts, and in Buffalo, New York. By 1893, Westinghouse had cut the frequency of the alternators from 133⅓ to 60 cycles per second. Such frequency is now standard in the United States.

In, 1885, at the time electric generating stations were being inaugurated, about 30 million tons of coal a year were being consumed by railroad locomotives and about 38 million tons consumed in industrial and domestic use. This latter amount is the equivalent of 89 billion kilowatt-hours of electric energy. In 1960 the electrical industry alone supplied 750 billion kilowatt-hours of energy; in addition, the equivalent of 3,000 billion kilowatt-hours of energy was supplied in other forms. This illustrates the growth of American industrial strength over the seventy-five-year period. It is estimated that by the year 2000 about 7,500 billion kilowatt-hours of energy will be required to meet the needs of this country.

In 1960, the average consumption of electric energy alone was 4,180 kilowatt-hours for every man, woman, and child in this country or 22,300 kilowatt-hours per average family per year. This amount of energy, if supplied by men working only with their hands, would require eighty-five men per average family. If all forms of energy—automobiles, natural gas, water supply, air lines, etc.—were included, the energy requirement would add up to that of 450 men per family. Much of this energy is hidden in the production of goods and services supplied to the family. The fact is, of course, that men working with their hands —with no machines—could produce only a very small portion of the goods and services that were produced and consumed in the year 1960.

In 1876, Alexander Graham Bell, a Scot who had settled in Boston, demonstrated a successful telephone. Manufacture was started early the next year, and nine months later 1,300 telephones were in operation. Telephones are now in nearly every home in America. Transmission between distant cities is generally by wireless communication. There are over 300,000 miles of telephone cable under the sea.

In 1964, the American Telephone & Telegraph Company inaugurated a telephone service between selected cities by which it is possible to view the person at the other end of the line. At present one must go to a station equipped for the purpose. In time, no doubt, the service will be in extensive use.

Heinrich Hertz discovered the presence of electromagnetic waves in 1887, following James Clerk Maxwell's prediction in 1865 that they would be found to exist. By this time telegraph and telephone communication systems were in wide use. In 1894, Guglielmo Marconi heard of Hertz's discovery and by 1896 he was transmitting and receiving wireless messages over a two-mile distance. He went to England to further his studies and by 1901 had successfully transmitted a wireless message across the Atlantic from Cornwall to Newfoundland. Lee de Forest in 1906 invented the triode vacuum tube. In 1918, Edwin H. Armstrong invented the superheterodyne. By 1919, broadcasting of the human voice was accomplished.

Principles involved in radio transmission have been further developed. The introduction of frequency modulation in place of amplitude modulation by transmitting at much higher frequencies has made possible the avoidance of much "static" due to storms and other causes. High frequency transmission was necessary also for the development of television, which, like broadcasting, has spread throughout the country and the world. Recent installations of Telstar satellites have made possible the relaying of radio and television signals for reception overseas. Eventually, the system will make possible worldwide transmission of television and high frequency radio. High frequency is being used to transmit to earth information gathered by satellites in outer space.

The social impact of this one segment of electrical engineering—electronic communication—is incalculable. Not only are people informed about events in distant places while they are happening but public opinion is, to a considerable degree, being molded and controlled by this medium. In most countries the medium is government-controlled, and public information and public opinion are limited by the governments for political purposes. In America, electronic communication has contributed greatly to the functioning of a large "democratic" society in complex domestic and international situations. The full educational potential of such communication has nowhere been realized.

Other developments of great importance have been made using high frequency radio waves. Radar makes possible the detection of moving objects on the surface or in the air, and of storm centers involving precipitation, by reflecting back from such objects a part of the beam sent out. This has become an important aid to aerial navigation. Very high frequency is employed in guidance and control of space vehicles. Another form useful for navigation at sea is an adaptation called loran, by which a ship may determine its position with considerable accuracy, with reference to two fixed stations on shore which are emitting continuous signals.

Bell Telephone Laboratories developed a transistor in 1948 through the discovery that certain crystals would perform the valve function of a vacuum tube. The advantage of the transistor is that it can be much smaller, requires less current, is much cheaper to manufacture, and is more rugged and reliable. It immediately made possible the "miniaturizing" of electronic sets of various kinds, especially the portable ones subject to vibration and shock.

The latest application of electronics has been in the development of computers. Devices have been built in which information may be stored and which will perform mathematical operations calling upon whatever part of the stored information is needed. Such a device lends itself to application as a control mechanism in which a program of sequences is stored awaiting a particular event which, when it occurs, will trigger the immediate performance of a predetermined sequence. One obvious use is to control high-speed operations by performing switching far more promptly and rapidly than manual switching could achieve.

When gases at high temperatures flow through a magnetic field, electrons flow across the gas stream. Attempts are being made to harness this principle in the field called magnetohydrodynamics. Temperatures on the order of 5,500°F are encountered; and the development of suitable materials becomes a major problem since steel melts at 3,000°F and copper at about 2,000°F. Indeed, the search for new materials is becoming a major project on many fronts.

Highly accurate surveys can now be made by determining distances by reflected light. The time required for a beam to travel to a target and back is measured with high precision, using the rate of oscillation in a crystal as the "clock." Accuracies of one part in 100 billion can be achieved on the clock in the observatory, but one part per million (or 3 inches in 50 miles) is the best field accuracy so far achieved. Triangulation as a basis for mapping is being done using this technique.

High frequency waves are being used instead of light waves in two other ways. Small objects may be "seen" in the electron microscope, in which magnifications of a hundred thousand are possible. On the other hand, distant objects may be "seen" with a radio telescope. With it, the planets and the moon are being studied, and the nature of their surfaces and their atmospheres is being investigated. The radio telescope is also being used to investigate the nature of outer space.

The uses to which electricity has been put in the past

hundred and fifty years have contributed greatly to man's well-being and his way of life and have expanded our culture and our fundamental knowledge. If one considers its many contributions to other branches of science through the development of better instrumentation, we can credit electrical application with many additional benefits.

Electrical engineering may be divided broadly into two areas, electric power and electronics. In the past, in many schools training for these two areas was divided to the point where courses in electronics have not been given to students intending to go into the power field. But because electronic devices are now employed widely in power controls, the electrical engineer of the future needs a broad and comprehensive training in the whole spectrum of electrical engineering.

This spectrum ranges from appliances and simple machines to computers, lasers, and radio telescopes. The theoretical background of electrical phenomena is based upon physics as represented by quantum mechanics, solid state physics, wave propagation, and plasma physics. In some schools the subjects are grouped under electrophysics and theoretical physics. In the field of electrophysics, the application of physics is more direct and perhaps more extensive than in any other engineering field. Physics, together with the necessary mathematics, forms a scientific background that is essential for the electrical engineer. This scientific background will not of itself, however, be adequate preparation for the practicing electrical engineer. He must understand materials, the mechanics of materials, the design of machines, fluid flow, and electro-mechanical mechanisms. If he is planning to enter the utilities field, he must understand the mechanical engineering involved in power plants and hydroelectric plants, and must in addition understand the problems of transmission of large amounts of power.

Recently, transmission lines of 750 kilovolts capacity, for both alternating and direct current, have been proposed for power transmission over distances of nearly 1,000 miles. The technical problems involved in such an undertaking are many and require a broad background of experience in addition to an extensive scientific knowledge.

The future of electrical engineering is bright indeed. To participate in the opportunities, a master's degree is essential and a doctor's degree is in most cases desirable. Advanced work in electricity lies close to the field of electrophysics. If the student intends to engage in engineering, the advanced study should be taken in an electrical engineering school. It should be interspersed with work in the summers, at least, in manufacturing or in the power field.

7

Chemical Engineering

One of the oldest fields of manufacture is ceramics, which is the historical foundation of chemical engineering. Ceramics includes the making of brick for building, pottery for utensils and ornament, tile for floors, walls and roofs, and glass for windows, utensils, and ornaments. Glass is made by fusing silica sands, with various minerals added for strength, color, and heat resistance. Bricks, tiles, and pottery are made by molding moist clay and baking or fusing it in a kiln.

Primitive people made brick by mixing straw with the wet clay and baking the hand-molded brick in the sun. This method was being used in Egypt in the earliest days of record, and is still in use there. The same procedure was used much later by the Indians in making adobe brick in the southwestern United States. The English builders in the sixteenth and seventeenth centuries built the walls of their houses in the Cotswolds from such a mixture, but instead of using bricks they laid the walls in successive layers, each layer in turn being allowed to bake in the sun.

In Mesopotamia, about 6,000 years ago, the Babylonians evolved a more advanced procedure in which the bricks were fired, rendering them stronger and more durable. Both they and the Assyrians developed a way of coating and re-firing to produce bricks with a colored face.

The Greeks did not use brick to the extent that the Babylonians, Assyrians, and Egyptians did, largely because they had excellent stone; but the Romans used it exten-sively, and introduced it into Britain and Germany 2,000 years ago. They also introduced kilns for burning the brick. When the Romans left Britain, brick was not used to any great extent until the fifteenth century. After the great fire of London in 1666, the city was largely rebuilt of brick.

Pottery was made by peoples in Neolithic (later Stone Age) times, for storing food and water, for cooking, and for ceremonial uses. Such pottery was simply made, with-out glaze, but often with ornament produced by painting, embossing, or modeling into fanciful shapes. Before 4000 B.C., the Egyptians had learned the art of glazing, using pottery "clay" with a high silica content, which resulted in a hard, translucent ware. From a painting, it is known that the potter's wheel, a round table mounted on a vertical spindle and turned with the foot, on which an urn or other vessel could be molded to a circular form while being ro-tated, was in use in Egypt about 1800 B.C.

With little basic change in method, except in the art of glazing, coloring, and refinement of form, the pottery mak-ing spread to Greece and Rome, whence it was carried throughout Europe. In France a finer pottery called porce-lain was developed, in an effort to match examples brought from China, and was given the name chinaware, or china. Kaolin (after *kao-lin*, meaning high hill, where the Chinese clay was mined), a white clay, is the basis of such porce-lain, combined with a feldspathic rock. It has been used in Germany and France since the beginning of the eighteenth century.

It is not clear where or when the use of lime and cement for masonry mortar began. The Egyptians fitted their large stone blocks closely enough so that their structures were stable without mortar in their particular climate. Although they used gypsum mortar for bedding face stones, they used lime mortar in rougher work 4,500 years ago.

The Sumerians built with sun-dried or burned bricks with very little stone, and they also used lime mortar. The Assyrians used a mortar with their stone which they must have made by burning limestone. It would appear that lime was in use throughout Mesopotamia at an early period. The Chinese used lime mortar in their Great Wall. The Romans, in addition to using the pozzuolano cement made from volcanic ash, also made concrete in their work in Germany; it is believed that they used cement made from trass, a volcanic rock found along the Rhine and in Belgium. There must have been something of a chemical industry among the ancients in the making of lime and cement, but the details of it are not recorded.

Common salt (sodium chloride) is a necessity of life. It occurs naturally as rock salt and as a prime constituent of the salts in sea water. Evaporation of salt from sea water has been an industry from earliest times. In Roman times, mercenary soldiers were paid by an allowance for salt, from which comes our word *salary* (Latin *sal*, salt), and our expression, "worth his salt." There is about a quarter of a pound of salt in a gallon of sea water. From this fact it has been computed that if all salt in the sea were recovered, it would equal a mass nearly fifteen times the land mass of Europe above sea level. Salt has long been used as a food preservative. It is required as an addition in diets based on cereals. Many industrial processes—including refrigeration, metallurgical treatment, and some chemical processes—involve its use.

Maritime peoples obtained the necessary salt for their diet by eating fish. Additional salt, for preserving fish and other foods, was obtained by evaporating sea water. In some inland localities salt springs were found; these led to the discovery of rock salt deposits, from which the saltiness originated. In modern times salt comes largely from the mining and processing of rock salt. At the present time a new interest is developing in the separation of the salt in sea water, not to obtain the salt, but to obtain fresh water. Because large areas in the United States, as well as in other parts of the world, are short of water for domestic, agricultural, and industrial uses, a large industry is in the making for processing sea water and furnishing fresh water.

In the latter half of the eighteenth century, in England, France, and Germany, various theories were held about the nature of chemical reactions. Imponderable properties, some described in the alchemists' lore, were thought to enter into reactions in an almost mystical way. In 1789, Antoine Laurent Lavoisier published his famous treatise on chemistry, which placed a foundation under chemical theory and established modern concepts from which chemical knowledge has grown prodigiously. Without such an ordering of thought, the developments of the past century and a half could not have been achieved.

Modern chemical processes on a commercial scale are believed to have had their origin in the Le Blanc method for making soda. In 1790, stimulated by a prize offered by the French Academy of Sciences, a physician named Nicolas

Le Blanc devised a process in which he treated common salt with sulphuric acid. This made a cake that, when fused with limestone and coke, produced sodium carbonate and calcium sulphate. Water was used to dissolve the sodium carbonate which was then concentrated by evaporation. Le Blanc, with the aid of the Duc d'Orleans, built a small plant capable of making about 500 pounds of soda a day. This process, which made a compound that was not only necessary to cooking, but indispensable for the making of soap, glass, and many other industrial chemical products, continued until replaced by the Solvay process invented in 1865 by Ernest Solvay, son of a Belgian salt refiner.

The Solvay process consists of the decomposition of ammonium bicarbonate and sodium chloride and the formation therefrom of ammonium chloride and sodium bicarbonate (baking soda). Actually, the process includes the use of ammonia, water, and carbon dioxide to form the ammonium bicarbonate, which is then made to react on the sodium chloride. A further refinement in the process is the conversion of the ammonium chloride into calcium chloride and ammonia; the calcium chloride is a chemical by-product and the ammonia is reintroduced at the beginning of the process.

An interesting fact about the development of the Solvay process is that in a striking way it introduced the element of economics into chemical processes. The commercial process, in design, construction, and operation, was far different from the achievement of the reactions in test tubes. Success of the process made an immense fortune for Solvay. His first plant, built at Couillet, Belgium, was still in operation ninety years later.

In 1840, Charles Goodyear discovered how to vulcanize

rubber. French explorers had discovered the rubber tree in the Amazon forest in 1735 and gum rubber had been made from the sap. The treatment necessary to give rubber a firmness and wearing quality, however, had not been discovered; and Goodyear was seeking such a process. One day, some gum rubber that had been mixed with powdered sulphur was accidentally dropped on top of a stove, and Goodyear had his answer on how to treat rubber. Goodyear first developed tires for bicycles, then soles for shoes, then boots and other wearing apparel. The need for automobile tires arose chiefly after the turn of the century, but the basic process for their manufacture had been developed in advance.

Of all the acids, sulphuric acid is the most widely used, partly because it is easily available and partly because it is cheap. It is not known when sulphuric acid, known as oil of vitriol, was first produced, but it was before 1600. It was first made commercially in Germany, by heating green vitriol (iron sulphate) and combining the sulphuric dioxide thus formed with air and water. Alum and other sulphates were also used. This acid was basic to the Le Blanc process, which produced hydrochloric acid. The modern method is to make it direct from sulphur, which is found in large quantities in the United States and elsewhere.

Two important ingredients are needed for high explosives—toluol, made from coal tar, and nitrogen, formerly obtained from nitrate rock. Nitrogen is also an important constituent in commercial fertilizers. A process was developed in 1902, at Niagara Falls, to "fix" nitrogen from the atmosphere, but it did not at once become commercial. In Germany, the Haber process of making ammonia from fixed nitrogen made possible a supply of explosive and fertilizers during the First World War, when German imports of nitrate rock from Chile were cut off. The United States was dependent upon the nitrate rock from Chile. To free this country from the necessity of shipping under wartime conditions, Mussel Shoals Dam was built in 1918 to produce power for making "fixed" nitrogen for explosives. By 1930, fertilizers were made from fixed nitrogen sources almost entirely.

In Florida, Tennessee, and South Carolina phosphate rock has been found. These phosphate beds are formed from the skeletons of prehistoric animals. The phosphate is in the form of tricalcium phosphate, which is insoluble. Treatment with sulphuric acid produces monocalcium phosphate, which in the fertilizer trade is known as superphosphate. Phosphate is also used to make matches and baking powder.

A huge industry has arisen since the invention of various plastics. The first of these was celluloid, which dates from 1872. This was followed by rayon, then bakelite. With the development of the process of polymerization came the development of nylon and other products used in either cast form or filament form. Materials such as rayon and nylon are largely replacing natural fibers in the textile field. Plastics are also replacing wood, leather, and metals for many uses.

One branch of the chemical industry is devoted to the making of pharmaceuticals, among them the "miracle" drugs; another to the processing of foods. Still another makes paper, cardboard, and packaging materials, a field shared with mechanical engineering. Piping and plumbing fixtures are also being made of plastics.

During the Second World War, the supply of natural

rubber from Malaya was cut off. Large plantations were growing it in Liberia and in South America, but these could not produce enough to meet the demand for rubber. Synthetic rubber factories were built in which butadiene was made from petroleum. Several synthetic rubbers are now widely used in place of natural rubber, although certain products are still made from natural rubber.

We have discussed the internal combustion engine and the use of gasoline as fuel for it. A whole family of petroleum fuels has been developed to fit the specific needs of internal combustion engines. Fuel oil has also been developed for domestic heating and for fuel in power boilers. Lubricants and asphalts are also made from petroleum, and both coal tar and petroleum are sources of dyes, flavoring extracts, perfumes, drugs, and many other specialized products.

The fact that chemical engineering processes are relatively new in the world's history is well illustrated by the rapid growth of the duPont Company. Young E. I. duPont was a bookkeeper and an assistant to Lavoisier in the powder factory of the French government. There he learned the best way then known to make gunpowder. After the French Revolution, in which Lavoisier lost his life, young duPont came to America, where President Jefferson urged him to set up a much-needed powder works. From this beginning, duPont has grown to the great industrial company it is today. It has practically spanned the political life of the United States, and its chemical competence dates from Lavoisier, "the father of modern chemistry."

The phenomenal growth of the chemical industry has been made possible by the extensive research carried on by the modern industry. Up to 1914, Germany led the world in chemical production. When the First World War began, and the supply of German chemicals was cut off, the United States and other countries were forced into intensive research to meet civilian and war needs. Fortunately, the needs were met. Since then, the United States has not only remained self-sufficient, but has been a world leader in the production of chemicals.

The chemical engineering field is expanding in many directions. Synthetic fibers in the textile field, the substitution of plastic parts for metallic parts in many machines, and the use of plastics in the container and packaging fields are instances of active expansion. The use of plastics in the building field has begun in Europe but has not yet gained headway in America. Many engineers believe this will be an active field in the years ahead. In Europe, entire houses have been built of plastics above the foundations, excepting only hinges and locks, and some metal reinforcing in the window frames. The advantages of such construction are that all the parts are factory made and that no painting is required either inside or out.

Preparation for chemical engineering includes a foundation in mathematics, physics, and chemistry. The chemical engineer must have an extensive background in inorganic, organic, and physical chemistry and biochemistry. He must also be trained in mechanical and electrical technology.

Specialization is common in chemical engineering. The more prominent branches are petroleum refining and petrochemicals, biochemical engineering, and plastics. Such specializations require advanced training to the doctorate.

8

Aeronautical Engineering

Man has always exalted the power of flight, endowing deities and celestial personages with such a gift. Many legends concerning flight have grown up, like the story the ancient Greeks tell of the escape from the Labyrinth by Daedalus and his son Icarus on artificial wings. Icarus, being young and eager, ignored the warnings of his father and flew too near the sun. The heat of the sun melted the wax by which his wings were attached and he plunged headlong into the sea.

Leonardo da Vinci shows a drawing in his *Codex* of a heavier-than-air flying machine which would propel itself by flapping its wings, the power to be furnished by pedals which the pilot would pump with his feet. There is no indication that Leonardo ever undertook to fly or even build such a machine. It was simply an idea.

The first recorded free flight of a man in the air was made on November 21, 1783, by J. F. P. de Rozier and the Marquis d'Arlandes in a balloon under the supervision of the Montgolfier brothers, Joseph and Jacques, who had constructed the balloon of waterproof linen, and had filled it with hot air. They ascended about 500 feet and traveled about 9,000 yards. On December 1 of that year, the French physicist Jacques A. C. Charles and a friend made a flight in a balloon of Charles' design, using hydrogen as the lifting gas. In this flight they rose 2,000 feet and traveled 27 miles. In a solo flight later that same day, Charles rose to about 10,000 feet. Henry Cavendish had discovered hydrogen in 1766 but it obtained its name from Lavoisier in 1783. Balloons have been used over the years since these early flights; the highest altitude, 113,739 feet with 99.6 percent of the earth's atmosphere below it, was achieved by the U.S. Navy.

The first elongate stiffened, powered balloon, called a dirigible, was operated under steam power by Henri Giffard in France in 1852. In 1900, Count Ferdinand von Zeppelin built his first dirigible, 420 feet long and capable of 18 miles per hour. This ship was succeeded by a series of dirigibles, each of a higher speed than the preceding one. Von Zeppelin made several flights across the Atlantic after the First World War, some with passengers. The United States Navy experimented with dirigibles in the early 1920s. Whereas von Zeppelin had used hydrogen, the Navy used helium to lessen the hazards of fire or explosion. The Navy discontinued its experiments with such craft after two dirigibles, the *Shenandoah* and the *Macon*, broke up in storms.

Nonrigid elongate powered balloons, called "blimps," were used for reconnaissance and shore patrol in the Second World War, since they are capable of low-altitude, low-speed flight. They are still occasionally used for local commercial sightseeing flights.

The first successful heavier-than-air machine was invented by two American brothers, Wilbur and Orville Wright, who flew the first manned flight on December 17, 1903, at Kitty Hawk, North Carolina. The flight achieved a distance of about 100 feet.

Before the Wright brothers' success, several people had attempted flight with heavier-than-air machines, and their experiments had a bearing on the work of the Wright brothers. In 1886 Otto Lilienthal made experiments with gliders in Germany. Beginning in 1896, a French-born American civil engineer, Octave Chanute, made and tested various designs of gliders with multiple planes using up to five pairs of wings, and finally settled on the biplane.

A third experimenter was Professor Langley of the Smithsonian Institution, who also began in 1896, and who used models with about a 14-foot wingspread. Associated with him was Charles Manly, a mechanical engineering graduate. In 1903, Langley built a full-sized airplane and equipped it with an engine designed by Manly. This was a 5-cylinder, water-cooled, radial gasoline engine which weighed, without accessories, only 125 pounds and developed 52 horsepower (hence weighing 2½ pounds per horsepower). After two attempts at launching, in each of which the plane collapsed, Langley gave up in discouragement.

The Wright brothers were bicycle mechanics in Dayton, Ohio. They read extensively and studied the reports of Lilienthal, Langley, and Chanute. They constructed a small wind tunnel with a throat 16 inches square and about 8 feet long, and with Chanute's help and advice tested over 200 wing configurations. Chanute was of the opinion that, at that time, the Wright brothers knew more aerodynamics than any other living person. They experimented with air-frames having one, two, and three pairs of wings. They finally settled upon a biplane with two opposed propellers with chain-drive from a four-cylinder, 12-horsepower engine which they built and which had a weight of nearly 16 pounds per horsepower. The whole biplane weighed about 750 pounds. The frame was of wood and the wings were of canvas. In 1905, using an engine with twice the horse-power, they flew twenty-four miles. In 1908, Wilbur Wright flew seventy-six miles.

The first takeoff from water was by Henri Fabre in France in 1910. In 1922, Sikorsky built in Russia the first four-engine airplane.

The piston engine, still used in aircraft, has been developed to produce one horsepower per pound of weight. The turbo-prop produces two horsepower per pound. The largest piston engine built has a rating of 3,500 horsepower. Turbojet engines are now being built with a rating of 12,000 pounds thrust at takeoff. Speeds now attained are several times the speed of sound, although no commercial flights have yet been made at supersonic speeds.

We can only touch upon the fact that the helicopter, which has a large vertically directed propeller, is capable not only of vertical takeoff and landing, but of hovering as well. Recently a monoplane aircraft has been built with engines directed vertically on takeoff, and then rotating to a forward position for flight.

In recent years we have witnessed the development of a missile capable of flights in excess of 5,000 miles. Men have also been put in orbit by both Russia and the United States. The thrust of a missile's engine at takeoff may be as much as 350,000 pounds.

It is interesting to note that the science of aerodynamics, on which present-day design in aeronautics rests, was not developed at the time the Wright brothers made their first flight, hence they were obliged to determine for themselves such principles as were necessary for their designs. As the design of airplanes advanced, the problems encountered required continual research efforts to provide enough knowledge to keep up with the pressing needs. The aeronautical engineer was thus often obliged to carry on his work in advance of a full scientific explanation of the phenomena involved.

Aerodynamics, which is a branch of the mechanics of fluids, is too complex to be treated adequately at the undergraduate level. Leading schools offer programs in this field extending to the doctorate. The undergraduate preparation required may be in mechanical, civil, or electrical engineering, or engineering physics.

9

Other Branches
of Engineering

In recent years, several specialized branches of engineering have been developing, some as fractionations from the larger fields we have been discussing, and others as new fields recently developed. One of these is agricultural engineering, in which the civil, electrical, and mechanical engineering applications to agriculture and food processing have been combined to prepare for specialization in such work.

In a similar way industrial engineering has become a specialty in which the principles underlying the operations of all forms of manufacturing and of production controls have been brought together. Industrial engineeering is being expanded in some of the leading schools to include the newer programming techniques of manufacturing and other operations under the control of computers. Such controls may extend to the balancing of inventories with sales and manufacturing. Ability to design computers for special purposes is essential.

A new field has evolved through the development of nu-

clear fission and fusion, called nuclear engineering. It embraces the development of reactors and other devices involving controlled radiation for producing power and for
other purposes. This is a field in which the older branches
of engineering also have an interest. Some schools treat nuclear engineering as a separate curriculum; others consider
it a component of one of the older branches of engineering.
As an example, the design, construction, and operation of a
nuclear-powered electrical generating station involves the
replacement of the conventional steam generator by a nuclear reactor; steam thus generated drives the turbine, as in
the coal-fired plant. Thus the need for the mechanical engineer is as great as before, only now he must have the ability
to design the nuclear reactor instead of the conventional
boiler. The principles of physics involved require additional study beyond that normally included in engineering
courses. Usually an adequate treatment of nuclear engineeering cannot be accomplished within a four-year curriculum, and it requires master's-level work.

A few colleges offer a curriculum in engineering physics.
This consists of much more physics than is found in other
curricula in engineering; but it also includes courses in materials of engineering and mechanics of materials, and design
courses not found in the typical undergraduate course in
physics. It has no counterpart in engineering practice. It is
especially useful to those continuing graduate study in
preparation for physics or for engineering research.

Geological engineering is another branch that has been
expanding in recent years. It is built around those segments
of geology of special use to engineering—geologic forma-
tions, rock strength and composition, rock mechanics, soil
mechanics, underground water systems, and geologic struc-

ture. Comprehensive programs in soil mechanics and foundations, together with supporting subjects in geology, have in the past supplied this need (except for the newer subject of rock mechanics, which is an advanced study available at only a few schools where elasticity and plasticity are comprehensively taught).

Refinery engineering embraces the engineering aspects of processing crude petroleum. It has been treated here as a part of chemical engineering.

There are several sub-branches of engineering that are held by some to be branches in themselves, such as welding engineering, tool-and-die engineering, materials engineering, automotive engineering, marine engineering, and the like. These are in fact specializations within the framework of mechanical engineering. I recommend training first as a generalist, after which specialization may be undertaken if desired.

10

The Development of Engineering

Engineering is a profession that covers the full sweep of history. It is a profession, moreover, that with each passing year is becoming more intimately involved in the very pattern of our culture. As we read world history and follow the development of, and improvement in, man's way of living, we see clearly that the achievements of engineers over the ages have profoundly molded the pattern of such development. If we were to strip them away, we would be living as men did before Babylonia. We would strip away much of the progress of at least 6,000 years.

Although the earliest engineering achievements occurred in a relatively small area extending from the mouth of the Persian Gulf to the lower Nile Valley, engineering influence spread to the west and north, where its fruits have flourished. The rich cultures of China and India did not embrace it. Today, two-thirds of the world's population is in Asia, which, except for Japan, is largely undeveloped industrially.

Only those parts of Africa that were settled by Europeans, chiefly in the temperate zones, have been developed industrially. Spain was not an industrial nation and its colonization in the New World did not carry with it any appreciable amount of industrialization. Although Africa and South America have great natural resources, the people, both native and colonial, were not industrially inclined. Today they are to varying degrees "underdeveloped."

The patterns of culture and of civilian life throughout the world today are varied and unevenly spread. They are the outgrowth of the extent to which engineering has been embraced and made a part of a progessive culture.

It would, of course, be foolish to assert that engineers alone are responsible for this great upsweep in civilization. Other forces, the achievements of other professions, the interlocking and cooperative efforts among the professions, have all played their part. The fact is, however, that the fate of rulers and of nations has hung upon the wealth produced largely through facilities and processes made available by the engineer.

Another lesson to be learned from this review of engineering progress is that our society depends completely upon maintaining a dynamic progress in our civilization. To mark time is to go backward. There never was a time when so many engineers—*good* engineers—were so urgently needed. Since wants on all fronts are constantly multiplying and satisfying them brings still further ones in their train, it would appear that, short of a cataclysm, the demand for engineers will continue to expand.

Our review points out that it is not accurate to say that the engineer's function is in the main that of "applying science for the benefit of man." The engineer is an innovator, a pioneer. He uses scientific principles when they are available, and wherever and whenever they will assist him in attaining his objective. In fact, in the realm of material facilities necessary for our cultural functions, the engineer is the chief medium of conveying and applying for public benefit those scientific principles which are applicable. But he is not and cannot be limited in his work to known scientific facts or principles. He has to reach out into new and untried fields to achieve new aids to man's progress, and he must master sufficient knowledge of them to maintain control over their function. He is a doer—with responsibility.

11

Aptitudes for an Engineering Career

No doubt you have asked yourself many times, "Is engineering for me?" If you know a good engineer, if you have talked with him and watched him work, you have a better chance to imagine yourself in engineering situations than many young men of your age. It is more likely that although you have heard something of engineering, you do not have a very precise image of engineering work, or of an engineer practicing his profession. To add to your difficulties, it is likely that you have no opportunity to see at first hand the differences between the many branches of engineering.

There are several important characteristics that successful engineers possess regardless of the branch of engineering in which they are practicing. The first of these is a strong desire to build something that will actually work. Would you like to be able to say that you designed the Golden Gate Bridge? Would you like to have developed the equipment by which the first Telstar message was sent from the United States to Europe? Would you like to be the chief engineer on a project to design a plant that will make new and better and cheaper synthetic rubber? Would you like to be the one to produce an alloy metal capable of use under higher temperatures than materials now available? If you have a strong desire to do any one of these things, or to participate in any similar achievement, you should by all means give thought to engineering as a career.

Another quality essential to a successful engineer is that he have the strength of character to stand responsible for his work. For example, after you examined a set of plans for a nuclear powerhouse, would you be willing, assuming the plans were in your opinion adequate and satisfactory, to state to a public official in a letter which he might wish to publish, that the powerhouse, if built as planned, would perform its function properly and would not endanger either life or property in the community? Would you be willing to sign such a letter knowing that in so doing, you would be staking your reputation and your future on being right? Would you, after examining the plans and the construction of a space vehicle and finding them satisfactory to you, be willing to state publicly, in writing, that you are satisfied with the design and the workmanship and that the astronaut may embark on a voyage in orbit with all safety devices and protection presently available to engineering? Would you be willing, assuming full and satisfactory knowledge were available of the design and construction of a large dam built across a stream above several large cities and flooding a broad valley for a hundred miles, to state that now the gates may be closed and the reservoir filled?

In making these decisions, it is, of course, assumed that you have adequate training in the sciences that are applicable; that you are fully conversant with the proper manufacture and construction of all important elements of the project; that you are competent to judge the workmanship done on components in many places and under a variety of conditions. Even so, you must have the kind of mind that appraises all these factors coldly, objectively, and in utter truthfulness. Finally, you must have the courage of your conviction to put your signature to a statement that clearly, candidly sets forth your judgment and opinion.

These questions I have been asking relate to later years, in the maturity of your professional life. More immediately, I suggest that you ask yourself whether you are ready to embark upon a program of difficult, exacting study and whether you are willing to subject yourself to the rigorous discipline of such training. The questions I have already asked you surely revealed a measure of the responsibilities you must assume in engineering practice. Are you willing to embark on a program of training yourself to assume such responsibility?

There are many vocations in which responsibilities and disciplines of the kind we have been discussing do not exist. On reflection, however, you will see that these same qualities are demanded by any *profession*. Consider the surgeon as he begins to open a patient's chest to perform surgery on the heart. Consider the judge about to pronounce sentence upon a defendant found guilty of a major crime. Consider the general as he orders 100,000 men to the attack. You are facing the broad question whether you want to be counted as a professional man.

But you should not be overwhelmed by the burdens of the profession. You will have as your support the knowledge you have acquired from the work of others, the careful checking of the possible risks involved and their reduction to manageable proportions, and the discipline that permits you to face difficult and dangerous situations with complete objectivity. It is a man's work—not a boy's. It is a real challenge. And in the end, there is the satisfaction of having discharged a real responsibility with complete success, of having performed a task requiring special abilities in such a way that others can and will say, "Well done!"

The devices, instruments, and systems with which an engineer works behave in accordance with one or more natural laws. A petroleum catalytic cracker can be designed and properly operated only through the understanding of the principles of physics and chemistry that are involved in the process. Since such a unit is in the neighborhood of 200 feet in height, it must, among other things, withstand strong winds as well as the internal temperatures and pressures to which it is subjected. Supporting this structure on a suitable foundation requires a thorough knowledge of geology and soil mechanics. You can see therefore that the design and operation of such a unit is not just an exercise in chemical reactions. A chemical engineer must possess an understanding of the forces that the unit must withstand.

In a similar way, the design and construction of a large steam-electric power plant involves a large number of actions which must be understood by the mechanical engineer. The steam generating unit may be nearly as tall as a twenty-story building. It may involve temperatures in the neighborhood of 3,000°F in the combustion chamber. It may have the capacity to evaporate 2 million pounds of water per hour and raise it to a temperature of around 900°F and 5,000 pounds per square inch pressure. Steam at such pressure and temperature is compressed to the density of a liquid and remains so until allowed to expand. A great many interlacing principles derived from physics and chemistry are involved in the behavior of such a generating unit.

In a similar way, the electrical engineer who designs and operates a large power system or the civil engineer who designs and constructs a large bridge or dam must deal with laws of physics and chemistry. In fact, all branches of engineering are based upon such principles.

To the extent that these basic principles of physics and chemistry can be stated as mathematical concepts, they can be studied with the aid of mathematics. Although not all engineering situations can be mathematically stated, a great many can; and thus mathematics becomes an important and necessary tool of the engineer. You have become familiar with algebra, geometry and trigonometry in high school, but you may not know very much about the origin of these branches of mathematics. We have discussed geometry earlier, and we know that it was developed by the Greeks and that the word means literally, "the measurement of the earth." Algebra has a different history; although the word itself is derived from the Arabic, its simpler principles were long known in India. Algebra seems not to have spread into Europe until the Moors invaded Spain. You have already learned how many interesting problems can be solved and how many queries can be answered by this fascinating branch of mathematics. It is the first of the branches to contribute to analysis. Although you are familiar with plane trigonometry, you may not know that spherical trigonometry, which deals with triangles on the surface of a sphere, was devised and used first. It was invented as a tool in the study of astronomy and was later extended to apply to triangles in a plane.

I mention these things here because you should realize why the engineers in ancient times could not solve their problems with mathematics. You should also understand the tremendous advantage you have over Aristotle and Archimedes and even Galileo through the mathematics which you have learned in high school.

But your most exciting experience with mathematics will begin with a study of the calculus. This branch of mathematics, which was invented independently by Newton and Leibnitz in the latter part of the seventeenth century, was brought to its present state largely during the eighteenth century. It was developed initially so that one could deal analytically with curves and was promptly extended to cover curved surfaces and curved solids. At that time there was a great backlog of unsolved problems awaiting the day when an adequate mathematical procedure should become available. Calculus fulfilled this need. You will find it no more difficult in its way than you found algebra when you first began to study it.

We have talked about your liking for mathematics as though it were a reality. Algebra and the calculus are exercises in orderly reasoning. Their mastery depends upon the step-by-step mastery of each successive assignment. It is very difficult to catch up if one gets behind. Here is an example of the importance of disciplining yourself to do your work promptly and thoroughly as you go along. You will then find that mathematics, instead of being drudgery, is really a lot of fun.

The precise laws that apply to ideal situations in physics lend themselves well to mathematical treatment, and their full meaning can be explored by mathematical procedures with verification in the laboratory. Many circumstances can then be studied that will be important foundations for later evaluation and decisions in engineering work, where situations will arise that cannot be fully expressed in mathematical terms.

All matter is made up of chemical elements, as you have learned in high school. The study of these elements and their interaction is essential to the practice of engineering. In college courses in chemistry, you will come to understand many things about the structure and behavior of matter.

I have discussed the subjects of mathematics, physics, and chemistry especially because these subjects are studied intensively for at least the first two years of an engineering course. It should be clear that one cannot embark upon an engineering project without an understanding of what he is doing. It should be possible to understand from the work you have had in physics, mathematics, and chemistry in high school that these subjects bear directly upon the use of materials, whether for a bridge or a transistor or a new chemical compound or a metal for some special use. You will understand, I am sure, that it is necessary to go a lot farther in these subjects than you did in high school. You may feel at times that you are in a long tunnel that seems to have no outlet ahead. I can assure you, however, that there is an outlet and that there is a great deal of satisfaction in having reached it in due course.

It is not uncommon for some students who have embarked on engineering to feel that the work is too hard or at least harder than they thought it would be. Some of this arises from the fact that they may not have gotten really on top of mathematics, physics, and chemistry in high school. I have already indicated that it requires determination and fortitude to achieve an engineering training, but it must be achieved if one wishes to really practice the profession. There is no short cut. A great many other people, feeling discouraged as you may on occasion, have preceded you successfully and have become great engineers.

12
Engineering Schools

The first engineering school in America was organized in 1802 for the training of a corps of engineer cadets at what is now the United States Military Academy at West Point. The beginnings were small and uncertain. Colonel Sylvanus Thayer, who had made a study of military academies in Europe, became Superintendent in 1817. He modeled the school largely after the École Polytechnique of Paris.

Captain Alden Partridge, alumnus and former Superintendent of the Academy at West Point, organized at Norwich, Vermont, the American Literary, Scientific, and Military Academy. It offered classical, agricultural, and surveying courses, and courses in "Mechanics, Hydraulics, Civil Engineering, including the construction of roads, canals, locks and bridges." In 1834, the academy was chartered as Norwich University, and in 1866 it was moved to Northfield, Vermont, its present location.

Amos Eaton in 1823 began the organization of Rensselaer Polytechnic Institute at Troy, New York, for the training of teachers of natural science. By 1835, he had developed it into what is believed to be the first school of civil engineering in the English-speaking world; it graduated four men that year with the degree of Civil Engineer.

Union College, in Schenectady, New York, began teaching some courses in civil engineering in 1845, and the University of Michigan began instruction in engineering in 1852. In that year a chair of mathematics and civil engineering was created at Yale in what became, in 1860, the Sheffield Scientific School. A three-year course in civil engineering was being taught there in 1856 and there was also offered (although only on paper) a course in mechanical engineering.

Thus only a handful of engineering schools existed in America before 1860. The few graduates played important roles in the engineering profession. The most prominent roles were taken by the Corps of Engineers of the U.S. Army, who prepared surveys preliminary to the building of the Chesapeake & Ohio Canal and of the Baltimore & Ohio Railroad. West Point was chiefly an engineering school until the Civil War.

Great impetus to the development of engineering schools was given by the Morrill Land Grant Act of 1862, which made grants to each state of public lands to establish a college for instruction in "agriculture and the mechanic arts." In the following ten years the number of such schools increased from six to seventy. The needs of the expanding economy have produced a steady advancement in the number and quality of engineering schools. It should be noted that nearly all the development and the many contributions of engineering education in this country have taken place over the relatively brief span of the past hundred years.

Engineers who are in responsible charge of engineering works are required to be licensed by the state or states in which they practice. The purpose of such licensing is to make sure that the engineer in charge is fully competent, in the interest of public safety.

A part of the requirement for registration is the successful passing of examinations, the last of which is taken after eight years of engineering experience. Graduation from an accredited engineering college accounts for four years of such experience. Nearly all the states accept accreditation by the Engineers' Council for Professional Development (ECPD), a body formed by eight leading engineering societies:

American Institute of Chemical Engineers
Institute of Electrical and Electronics Engineers
American Institute of Mining, Metallurgical
   and Petroleum Engineers
American Society of Civil Engineers
American Society of Mechanical Engineers
American Institute of Aeronautics and Astronautics
National Council of State Boards of Engineering
   Examiners

Accreditation is given for each approved curriculum at a given engineering college. Some colleges have but one accredited curriculum while others have all their curricula accredited. A curriculum consists of a required sequence of courses leading to a first engineering degree, as, for example, Bachelor of Electrical Engineering.

There are 247 engineering schools in the fifty states, District of Columbia, and Puerto Rico, 167 of which have at least one curriculum accredited by ECPD. There is at least one such accredited school in each of the fifty states and in the District of Columbia and Puerto Rico. The state with the largest number is New York State, with sixteen schools. Anyone wishing to obtain a list of accredited schools and curricula may write the Engineers' Council for Professional Development, 345 E. 47th Street, New York, New York, 10017.

The enrollment for the bachelor's degree in accredited engineering colleges in the fall of 1965 was 215,892; of these 1,896 were women. In 1957, there were 229,656 so enrolled. The corresponding freshmen classes were 67,071 in 1957, and 67,376 in 1963, a gain of 305 in an eight-year period.

On a national average, only about half of those in the freshman class ultimately graduate in *engineering*. About half of the remainder shift to other fields and graduate in them. The remaining quarter includes students who run out of funds, or who leave because of health or for a variety of other reasons besides academic failure. Such statistics indicate that academic failure is not the main cause of leaving engineering. First degrees given in 1959 in engineering were 33,695 and in 1965, 30,265, a gain of 839 in six years.

At the beginning of the decade 1960–1970 an estimate of the need for engineers for the period was made by the National Science Foundation with the aid of the Bureau of Labor Statistics. It was estimated that in 1960 there were 822,000 engineers in the country, and that by 1970, 1,374,-800 would be needed, an increase in ten years of 552,800.

It is important to note that this means an average increase per year of about 55,000 engineers. Assuming a professional life of fifty years, the average annual replacement due to death and retirement would be 16,000. In addition, I estimate that about 4,000 engineering graduates per year leave the profession for some other field. With only 30,000 graduating a year, there are thus only 10,000 available each year to *increase* the total number of engineers. This 10,000 should be compared to the 55,000 overall annual increase needed as estimated by the National Science Foundation and the Bureau of Labor Statistics.

These figures offer the best factual evidence at present available that the supply of engineers coming into the profession is considerably below the estimated requirements. Since the class that enrolled in the fall of 1965 will not graduate until 1969, there is no likelihood that the number of graduates will rise much above 30,000 a year by 1970. If there is a greater rise beyond that date, I estimate that it will be only a modest increase.

It is instructive to consider in more detail where in 1960 the Bureau of Labor Statistics thought the increase in need would be during the 1960s. The aircraft, missile, and spacecraft industries would need an increase of 67,000 for all engineering categories, whereas manufacturing as a whole would need an additional 350,000. Thus the spacecraft field requires only about 19 percent of the estimated need. In fact, less than 5 percent of the total number of engineers are now engaged in the aircraft, missile, and spacecraft industries.

It is becoming clearer each year that four years of engineering training do not adequately prepare one for the practice of engineering in its more general form. In 1954, 4,130 master's degrees were given; in 1963, the number was 9,600, or more than double the number nine years before. Many industries encourage their employees to get a master's degree at a nearby school, and some students get a master's degree before entering engineering practice. Some schools do not give the first engineering degree until the end of the fifth year.

The pressure for better trained engineers is here to stay. In planning your engineering career, you should allow at least five years for your formal educational program. What arrangement of degrees you get is less important than the quality of the training.

Although from that fact all engineering schools with ECPD accreditation would seem to be alike in quality, this is not the case. What is attempted by ECPD is to establish a *minimum* below which accreditation is not given. No rating of accredited schools is undertaken by any agency.

There are various ways in which some idea of the quality of a school may be obtained. Popularity of schools is often mistaken for an indication of their quality. While a good football team may be desirable, that in itself does not guarantee a good engineering education, although it is possible to have both.

A very sound indication of the quality of an engineering school is the reputation of its engineering graduates. An appraisal of this kind is best obtained by consulting a friend in engineering practice.

Nearly all engineering schools in the Northeast require trigonometry for entrance, so that the calculus may be started in the first term of the freshman year. Many schools in other parts of the country are instituting similar requirements, at least to the extent of requiring an additional term if the student enters without trigonometry. Some high schools are now offering the calculus.

A considerable number of schools offer no graduate work. Usually this is because of lack of facilities, staff, or finances. Another large group of schools give graduate work only through the master's degree. The catalogue of each school should indicate to you whether graduate work is given, and in what field. It is not uncommon for students to take a bachelor's degree at one institution and a master's degree at another. In this way, one widens his contact with professors in his field.

The school of your final choice may be selected by a combination of quality, availability, and cost. If you are planning a five-year sequence, and I strongly recommend that you do, I advise you to be somewhat more selective in choosing the school for graduate work than in choosing the school for the first degree. When the time comes for choice of graduate work, you will have the assistance of your professors, who will be able to give you much information about various schools through their own knowledge and acquaintance. You may, on the other hand, choose a school which has an integrated five-year program to the baccalaureate degree.

In choosing schools for five-year sequences, there is one factor you should fully understand. In many graduate schools it is not possible to enroll for graduate work if you are in the lower half of your class at the time you acquire the bachelor's degree. Also, some schools offer master's programs only to those who are intent upon a career in research. Such a program may not, and in my opinion does not necessarily, fit the requirements for training for general practice.

13

Engineering Education

Formal education at the college level attempts to acquaint the individual with the knowledge, thoughts, and experiences of others who have gone before him. For purposes of the present discussion, we may divide the subjects involved in various ways. One way would be to separate the obviously practical ones from those that have less tangible application. Another grouping that we might make is to separate subjects dealing with material and inanimate things from those that deal with people, their behavior, their thoughts, and their experiences. Still another way would be to separate those subjects dealing with fact from those dealing with opinion.

You will find that some of these subjects attract you more than others, and because of this you will have the tendency to favor some of them over others. It is common experience, for example, to find that certain individuals are naturally attracted to people, while others are attracted to studies relating to inanimate things. Some individuals are more attracted to abstract and philosophical subjects while others are more intent upon pursuing purely practical matters.

In the practice of engineering you will, of course, be

dealing with materials such as metals and chemical elements, and with forms of energy. You will also be dealing with people, their ideas, the forces that motivate them, circumstances that please or disturb them, factors that produce loyalties or dissension, their ambitions, and their differences in character traits. You will also encounter situations in which philosophies and concepts of social systems, political institutions, or the cultural heritage will predominate. You will find times in which some one of these factors may be a pivotal point in your action before you are permitted to carry on with your technical work. You will very frequently find that your technical work is interwoven inseparably with one or more of these human relationships. You cannot afford, therefore, in planning your education, to exclude from your training any of these factors, or to emphasize some at the expense of others. Those which at first seem less interesting to you should be made the subject of special attack until you have achieved an understanding of the role they play in the total scope of your life work.

A liberally educated man can discuss a variety of subjects ably and with facility, and while doing so, can remain objective and detached from preconceptions and biased points of view. This is a goal worth striving for. The educational process should help one to attain it. Obviously it requires an understanding of a variety of points of view and a tolerance and fairness in weighing the value of each. It requires an orderly mind—a mind that is disciplined. It must be a mind that is alert, curious, perceptive, and completely honest.

The contributions to this educational goal must come from the subjects studied and an awareness of their values.

A vital factor is the ability to express oneself in an orderly and fluent fashion. The way to articulate expression either in writing or in speech is to learn to write well. The engineer has great need to be articulate because he must explain his work to others accurately, clearly, and convincingly. Writing is a creative skill, and insofar as it promotes easy flow of ideas it is useful to the engineer in his creative work. E. B. White says, "The act of composition, or creation, disciplines the mind; writing is one way to go about thinking, and the practice and habit of writing not only drain the mind but supply it, too." *

In his *Autobiography*, Benjamin Franklin tells how at the age of fifteen, already an experienced printer, he started molding his style of writing.

> About this time, I met with an odd volume of the *Spectator*. I had never before seen any of them. I bought it, read it over and over, and was much delighted with it. I thought the writing excellent, and wished if possible to imitate it. With that view, I took some of the papers, and making short hints of the sentiments in each sentence, laid them by a few days, and then, without looking at the book, tried to complete the papers again, by expressing each sentiment at length, and as fully as it had been expressed before, in any suitable words that should occur to me. Then I compared my Spectator with the original, discovered some of my faults, and corrected them. But I found I wanted a stock of words, or a readiness in recollecting and using them, which I thought I should have acquired before that time, if I had gone on making verses; since the continual search for words of the same import, but of different length to suit the measure, or of different sound for the rhyme, would have laid me under a constant necessity of searching for variety, and also have tended

* William Strunk and E. B. White, *The Elements of Style*, Macmillan, 1959, p. 56.

to fix that variety in my mind, and make me master of it. Therefore I took some of the tales in the *Spectator*, and turned them into verse; and, after a time, when I had pretty well forgotten the prose, turned them back again.

I also sometimes jumbled my collection of hints into confusion, and after some weeks endeavoured to reduce them into the best order before I began to form the full sentences and complete the subject. This was to teach me method in the arrangement of the thoughts. By comparing my work with the original, I discovered many faults, and corrected them . . .

Franklin's method of studying Addison's style and making it his own is a method that you may well follow in the study of any subject. He read the text, then laid it aside; then he tried to reconstruct it on his own. This is an excellen way of mastering any subject, whether it be an exposition in mathematics or physics or history or literature.

Whether your course in English composition requires it or not, I suggest that you buy a small book, *The Elements of Style* by Strunk and White. I urge you to keep it near you, to read and reread it and to follow its precepts. It will serve you well. I also suggest that you add another book for frequent reference concerning this business of writing, *Modern English Usage*, by Fowler. You should form the habit of reading widely. If you persist in such a habit, you will one day become a learned and wise man.

Herbert Hoover, in telling of his experiences as a mining engineer, recounts that while taking a prolonged journey into the interior of China, he took with him a box of books containing cheap paper translations of Balzac, Dumas, Zola, Victor Hugo, Rousseau, and Montaigne, for the purpose of gaining an introduction to French literature. On later travels he read from Voltaire, Mirabeau, the Encyclopedists, and other thinkers. He tells us that on other occasions, he read more generally on "Chinese history, Confucius, Mencius, economics, sociology, fiction, Plato, Shakespeare, Schiller, Goethe." * Many engineers and other professional people take advantage of travel and leisure time to widen their range of reading.

Another useful subject, which really should be studied in high school, is Latin. Its orderly grammar aids in the understanding of English grammar, and so many of our words have come from the Latin that a knowledge of it contributes to a better feeling for many English words. It will be helpful to study French, German, and Spanish either in high school or in college. They are useful in reading both technical and general literature.

You will profit by a course in psychology. The learning process is a fascinating subject of study, and you will find a knowledge of psychology useful, not only in learning how to study, but later on in engineering practice, when it will help you to present your ideas to others in ways that will appeal and be readily understood. It is also an excellent way to begin the study of how people think and behave. You will not have all the answers, but you will become more perceptive and more understanding of other people.

Every engineering project involves the cost of production or of construction, the cost of operation and of maintenance, and the method by which income may be derived, not only to pay these costs, but to pay interest on the investment together with a reasonable profit. Thus an engineer should be well grounded in the principles of economics. Economics will also prepare him for his later

* *Memoirs of Herbert Hoover. Years of Adventure*, Macmillan, 1953, pp. 35–47.

reading in the fields of banking, the issuance of securities, corporate finance, and international monetary systems. It is desirable that he should also study the history of the labor movement and its economic and social implications.

When we were reviewing the historical aspects of engineering discoveries and achievements, we did not have the time to place them in the context of political and social history. You will find it interesting to relate the engineering developments to other circumstances of the times in which they occurred. It is important to know some of the consequences of these engineering events; and you will find that history acquires a special meaning when approached in this way. Political history makes little mention of notable engineering achievements that, as we have seen, have had a profound effect upon the development of our culture. Political history also often fails to mention many economic factors that have exerted great influence upon the course of civilization. Reading the history of science and technology together with economic, political, and social history will give a far more balanced appreciation of past events than can possibly be acquired from political history alone. It will also strengthen your understanding of the place of your profession in modern society.

In planning your college program, you should arrange to conserve your time while in college by taking those courses that open new fields to you, or ones that you are not likely to master successfully by yourself for lack of laboratory facilities or teaching assistance. Before the twentieth century many people, and in fact most professional people, acquired their education without benefit of college. The technological pace is now much too fast for you to prepare in that manner for the engineering of today or the future, but there are subjects which may be left for subsequent reading when your own maturity of experience and thought will permit you to pursue them more profitably and in more depth.

It is necessary that you embark upon your study of mathematics at the outset of your program. At the same time, or very soon thereafter, you should start the study of physics and chemistry. These are the subjects that you no doubt have heard about as being tough, those that "nobody can understand." Assuming that you made a good grade in high school or preparatory school in these subjects, and assuming that you are of average intelligence, I can say quite emphatically that you should have no difficulty with these subjects. What you may have difficulty with is the task of forcing yourself to keep up to date with your assignments. These subjects are like a ladder: there is no shortcut to the top; the easy, in fact the only way is to take a rung at a time. Benjamin Franklin's formula for mastering style works perfectly for studying these subjects. If you will follow this simple method in your courses in science and engineering, I can assure you of a position not lower than the top quarter of your class.

Self-discipline is not acquired easily; the necessity for it is not peculiar to engineering. It is a quality necessary to success in any field, whether it be in a profession or in athletics.

Some students embark upon engineering programs not yet certain that they wish to take an engineering course. They have the notion that the first year or so will reveal the nature of engineering, and that they will "try it and see how it goes." This is a good idea only in theory; in practice, the early courses in mathematics, physics, and chemistry are science courses and reveal to one *little or nothing about the practice of engineering.* These courses will prove that discipline is a part of the preparation for engineering —or for science. Mastery of these subjects is necessary for engineering, but by themselves, they will disclose to you little of the nature of engineering.

It is desirable, if you can do so, to explore sufficiently the nature of engineering before you come to college and thereby gain a fairly firm conviction about your choice of engineering and of a branch of engineering. If you cannot do this, I suggest that you plan to work at engineering jobs during your college summers. They will tell you more about the nature of engineering than freshman or sophomore courses can.

The early science courses furnish necessary background for a series of courses in branches of science peculiar to engineering, such as dynamics, thermodynamics, mechanics of solids, fluid dynamics, combustion, aerodynamics, electrophysics, electronics, and the like. These subjects are the scientific foundation for engineering design and research. Not until you reach these courses can you get an idea of the *scientific* aspects of engineering. How these courses are used in engineering situations will hardly be disclosed to you before the fourth year.

If you have chosen a combined program leading to a Bachelor of Arts and a Bachelor of Engineering, which will take five or six years, you will be completing this program at one institution. Some colleges have a five-year curriculum leading to one degree, a bachelor's in the appropriate field of engineering, and a few have an integrated five-year program granting both a bachelor's and master's degree in engineering. When such a program is integrated over the five years, it is best to complete the program at one institution. In the event that only a four-year program is offered and further work may be done in the graduate school, it is suggested that the graduate work be done at some other institution than that at which the undergraduate work is taken; in this way one has the benefit of contact with two different faculties.

If graduate work is intended for the purpose of specialization, the school best equipped in the specialty should be the one chosen for such study. This is especially true if you intend to study for the doctorate.

You should adopt the attitude that the university or college you attend is offering you a golden opportunity to stimulate your intellectual curiosities and thirsts. I urge you to make the most of this opportunity.

The formal education the engineer receives is only the foundation. It introduces him to the principles underlying engineering and it provides him with the means for continuing study throughout his professional life. It is not possible to provide collegiate instruction in many techniques that can be better learned on the job, in the plant, or in the office. Furthermore, the field is continually advancing in knowledge and methods. Weekly periodicals, monthly proceedings, and new books must be read to keep abreast of expanding technology. Equally important is the general reading that brings perspective to the political, social, and economic conditions that surround engineering activities, and to which the profession makes a contribution. The successful engineer, like all accomplished professional men, is a student throughout his life.

14

The Role
of the Engineer

Let us assume that a public agency approached a consulting civil engineer to discuss the possibility of a toll bridge or tunnel across Delaware Bay. What part in such a venture does the engineer play?

Obviously, the first step is to make a feasibility study. The engineer would indicate his fee for such a study, and if a figure is agreed on, the agency would engage him by contract to make the study. The agency is the client and he is the consultant.

The feasibility study of such a project requires a thorough investigation of all the factors that would importantly affect the construction and operation of such a bridge or tunnel. An appraisal of the highway network would be necessary. This would involve not only the local traffic, but also that to and from the nearby cities; and it would also include through traffic between New England, metropolitan New York and Philadelphia, to the north, and Norfolk and the southeastern states to the south. Furthermore, an estimate of growth of traffic over the next ten and twenty years would be necessary. This in turn would involve estimates of population growth of the entire area served by the crossing—namely the Eastern Seaboard. Estimates of the traffic would be necessary to determine the capacity to be provided; they would also be the basis of tolls to be charged, from which the cost of the crossing would be financed.

Studies would then be undertaken to plan connections with the existing network of highways on both sides of the bay, both to achieve the best flow of traffic and to determine the location of required new approaches in terms of convenience for users and benefits to areas served. Here again population growth and regional development would have to be studied carefully.

The physical conditions of the area would be determined. The geology of the Bay area is generally known and such information is available from state and federal surveys, but these studies would not be sufficiently precise; and as soon as preliminary routes were selected, borings would be required to determine whether a heavy structure could be supported on the underlying strata. The U.S. Corps of Engineers has jurisdiction over navigable waterways; from the nearest district office the channel and clearance requirements could be obtained. Storm conditions in the area could be obtained from the Coast Guard and the Weather Bureau. The state agencies that control fisheries, oyster beds, and other aquatic activities would have to be consulted for possible restrictions on the proposed work.

From these various data, one or more preliminary sites would be chosen. A study would then be made of the nature of the structure required at each site. The amount of traffic expected would determine the width of the roadway. The width of the channel required for navigation would determine the nature and size of the span at that point, if a bridge were built; or, if a tunnel were built, the length of a tunnel under the channel. The Chesapeake crossing at Norfolk comprises both bridges and tunnels.

Preliminary estimates would next be made to determine the cost of the structure and its approaches. The question could now be answered whether, at reasonable tolls, the traffic on the bridge would be sufficient to earn interest on the investment and eventually to amortize the cost. The bankers arranging the financing would require of the engineer a statement of his prediction of feasibility and his estimate of earnings.

Assuming that the financial aspects seem favorable to the client, the next step would be to direct the engineer to proceed with detailed design of the structure at the optimum site and to indicate properties that must be acquired and permits that must be obtained. A suitable fee would then be agreed upon.

With the plans and the financing completed, bids would be requested from contractors who could qualify. If the engineer has made a reasonable estimate of the cost of the structure, the bids should be close to or within his estimate. Assuming this to be the case, the contract would be let and the job would move forward.

The engineer must now supervise the work through inspectors placed on various parts of the job. It is his responsibility to see that what was intended in the plans and specifications is complied with by the contractor. From time to time he issues certificates of completion on which the contractor may be paid for those portions of the work then finished. Upon completion of the work, he issues a final certificate on the basis of which final payment to the contractor is made.

The consulting engineer we have been discussing here serves as the chief engineer of the project. On such a large project as this, the chief engineer requires a considerable engineering staff. His assistant engineer of surveys would have the task of establishing the alignment and the location of each of the piers or other supports across several miles of open water. He would probably determine distances by equipment using the radar principle. The assistant engineer of surveys would, of course, need a staff of junior engineers to assist him. There would be an assistant engineer in charge of foundations for heavy piers constructed near the channel to support an overhead span; an assistant engineer in charge of the erection of the span; an assistant engineer in charge of highway approaches, who would also direct the paving of the main structure; and an assistant engineer in charge of inspection of all materials. Each of these assistants would have under him a staff appropriate to the amount of work in his charge. Some of these would be technicians; others would be junior engineers qualified for specific engineering tasks (and gaining experience by watching other work going on around them). The assistant engineers would report to a resident engineer who would be in charge of all field work.

In the office there would be a staff of engineers and draftsmen engaged in the design of the structure and the review and approval of all shop and erection drawings furnished by the contractor or his subcontractors and materials suppliers.

We have been discussing an instance of private or consulting practice in structural engineering. Civil engineers practicing in other areas, such as sanitary engineering or hydraulic engineering, would have offices organized in much the same manner and their field work would be carried out along similar lines. A civil engineer specializing in large hydroelectric plants would have on his staff a chief mechanical engineer and a chief electrical engineer who would supervise design and construction in their respective fields.

Highway construction is usually carried out by state highway departments or by county or city departments. In a state department, there would probably be a chief highway engineer and under him would be district engineers, each having complete jurisdiction over work in a given portion of the state—subject, of course, to the chief's approval. In some states the chief engineer reports to the Commissioner of Highways, usually a political officer, or to a Superintendent of Public Works, also a political officer but likely to be an engineer.

While there are some consulting engineering firms that do work in mechanical, electrical, and chemical engineering, a considerable portion of such work is done by the engineering organizations in industrial companies. Such a department or division is usually headed by a vice president of engineering who functions as the chief engineer of the company. He usually has charge of design, development, and research, but not manufacture, which would be under a different vice president.

In mechanical engineering, design plays as important a part as it does in civil engineering, especially when dealing with large units. Small components may be "developed" at the bench and tested out immediately but this cannot be done with large components because of cost.

Suppose a large oil company contemplates building a chemical plant for the manufacture of a new chemical compound, intended for use by other manufacturers as raw material. The research and development laboratory has already made extensive tests to determine the properties of the proposed compound, involving engineering evaluations and judgments at all levels from the study groups through the director of the laboratory to the vice president in charge of engineering and research. A market survey must be made, in which certain independent agencies and producers will try samples of the material in preliminary practical applications to determine the suitability of the compound for a variety of uses. If these trials appear promising, and if a suitable profit can be made by both manufacturer and processer, a report to management is then prepared, recommending further development and giving data, evaluations, and forecasts based on them. A pilot plant is then authorized, of enough capacity to supply the processers with sufficient compound for production of finished products at a practical manufacturing rate. More accurate costs may now be determined by both manufacturer and processer. If the costs are satisfactory, a full-scale plant is authorized; if they are not satisfactory, further refinements in production are developed until the costs are brought into proper range.

The evaluation of each step depends upon the abilities and judgments of a series of engineers at different levels, extending up through the vice president. Each engineer in the chain of authority bears a proportionate share of responsibility if the plant does not perform successfully in terms of either the quality of the chemical, or satisfactory cost of production. Based upon the reports submitted, top management may authorize large sums of money for the plant.

The design of the plant may be handled in one of two ways: it may be developed by the company's own engineering staff, or it may be turned over to an outside engineering firm to carry out. In either case drawings and specifications are produced and must be approved by various engineers of the company in charge of specific features of the work before the contract for the construction of the plant is let. The engineers of the company are thus responsible for whatever the company asks the contractor to do; and the plans and specifications, in setting forth with precision the construction requested, serve as a basis for fixing the responsibility of the contractor to furnish exactly what is called for.

The design and construction of plants for other industrial production, whether in the electrical, mechanical, or metallurgical industries, are carried out in the same manner as that described for chemical manufacture. In this case, however, instead of a pilot plant, a single machine or a sequence of machine operations must be subjected to rigorous testing before a complete factory operation is undertaken. The trials involve costs, quality of product, life of the machines, labor required for their operation and maintenance, and market acceptance of the finished product. The judgments required are not merely technical, but involve human factors and economic considerations as well.

To prepare for such broad responsibilities, a general as

well as a technical education is essential; but no engineer can grow with his job and with his times if he does not continue studying developments in his field, and read widely of social and economic trends and changes. Automation is an example of an engineering development involving many aspects of social and economic consequences.

15

Beginning the Practice of Engineering

Colleges and universities generally operate placement offices for their graduates and for those soon to graduate, as well as for those about to receive advanced degrees. Companies that maintain engineering staffs usually send one or more representatives to campuses to interview seniors. The placement offices maintain a file of literature about companies who will be recruiting, and students interested in interviews may sign up for those companies by whom they would like to be interviewed. Small companies and small consulting firms that normally may not send representatives are frequently alerted by the placement officer when a student desires an interview.

Placement offices also help to arrange the kind of summer employment that contributes to engineering experience. Not infrequently summer jobs mature into permanent jobs after graduation.

In a large company there are various departments which require an engineering degree. Such a company probably has a manufacturing department, a sales department, and possibly a research and development department. Some of the very large companies have a training program through which all men who come straight from college must pass. This training program is intended to acquaint the new recruit with the company organization and policies, the nature of its business, and the different departments that require the services of engineers.

Some young graduates have the idea that the sales department is "where the money is," and that sales engineering requires a salesman's personality with little engineering capability. This is far from the fact. It is the function of the sales engineer to help the customer on some project or production program, or on the design of a new facility. The sales engineer becomes virtually a consultant to the customer. He does, of course, try to fit his company's products into the customer's plans where appropriate, and in some cases he may find that an item could be better modified to fit the customer's needs. This requires experience in the use of his company's products and a knowledge of its manufacturing capabilities. The sales engineer must also understand the kind of plant and facilities needed for the manufacturing operation contemplated by the customer. This engineering work cannot be performed by a raw recruit. Also, it takes more than a pleasing personality: it demands sound technical training, experience, and judgment.

The engineer in the manufacturing department usually starts out as a timekeeper, an inspector in quality control, or an assistant on the superintendent's staff running errands and the like. Eventually he becomes concerned with developing improvements in machines and processes, for the purpose of improving a product or reducing the cost of its manufacture. If the young engineer appears to have qualities of leadership and the ability to get along with people under a variety of circumstances, and also has the ability to keep his head while under pressure, he may be started on the managerial ladder. A good executive will see that a young man on the managerial ladder gets a range of experience and becomes seasoned in judgment and in the ability to handle people. He will keep the young man moving along up the ladder as rapidly as his capabilities are proven, but not so fast as to expose him to situations for which he has developed neither experience nor talent. During this early experience in management, the young engineer will need to make a real study of the rules and regulations involved in labor relations.

The engineer who intends to go into research and development will find that advanced degrees are mandatory. The doctorate is generally looked upon as evidence that its holder has had some high-level training in research. The prospective employer will want to know of the applicant what his major and minor fields of study were, what the topic of his thesis was, and the professor under whom he wrote it. The employer will realize that the candidate knows little or nothing about the company's business, unless before acquiring the doctorate he had employment in the same or a similar company. Most likely the candidate has had only summer jobs in which to gain engineering experience and it is probable that during graduate work he had no summer employment outside the university.

Such a situation may be difficult for both employer and employee. The employer cannot move his new man ahead fast on development work, if that is the assignment, because of the employee's lack of experience with the plant processes involved. At the same time the employee is ambitious and is overtrained for the job he is given. Patience and understanding are needed on both sides. All too frequently the employee weakens under the pressure and decides to go elsewhere. It is likely that such a move would be a mistake on his part until he could point to several years of successful experience; and if he could do so, it is pretty certain that his present employer would not want him to leave.

Government Employment

A number of government departments employ engineers. The Army Corps of Engineers, the Navy's Bureau of Yards and Docks, the Signal Corps Laboratories, the Bureau of Reclamation, the Bureau of Standards, the Bureau of Mines, the Coast and Geodetic Survey, National Aeronautics and Space Administration, and other agencies employ engineers of various kinds and in various capacities. Inquiry should be made of such agencies to determine what categories are open.

Such employment is through the Civil Service. It is usually necessary to take an appropriate examination for the lower grades. Upper grades will require evidence of experience and training appropriate to the job and to the agency. A letter addressed to the agency at Washington, D.C., will bring information concerning opportunities and procedures for making application.

Research

Many companies have research and development departments. There are also companies organized solely for research and development, and some government bureaus at both the federal and state levels are concerned chiefly with research and development. In addition, there are research laboratories in the universities.

Most industrial research is concerned with the achievement of a new process or product. Principles are explored, but chiefly with the objective of finding a result that will have commercial value. When the outcome of such research looks commercially promising, the next phase consists of readying it for ease of manufacture and for customer adaptation. This latter phase is called development. Development laboratories are also engaged in improving and perfecting the existing line of products.

There is another area of investigation that is called basic or pure research (meaning research in basic or pure science). Here the objective is not the achievement of a commercial product but rather the discovery and clarification of natural laws. A few large companies have departments of basic research, but such companies must be willing to risk capital in the hope of a discovery that may open areas of new knowledge that would lend themselves ultimately to commercialization. Large chemical and pharmaceutical companies have special need for such laboratories. Some companies that do not have a basic research laboratory have a few people in their applied research department who devote most of their attention to fundamental problems as a reinforcement to those who are working chiefly on applied research.

Both basic and applied research may be found in government laboratories, especially at the federal level. The Bureau of Standards is such an organization. State laboratories—for example, highway laboratories and laboratories connected with state boards of health—exist largely for the purpose of monitoring jobs or activities being carried on under state regulations.

It is easy to see that at times all three functions, basic and applied research, and development, are of interest to, and are participated in, by engineers. Research that is hemmed in by precise requirements of usage or manufacture is frequently far more difficult than that which is not so restricted. Fundamental concepts may be known for many years before application under tightly controlled conditions can be made to work. This was true in the development of electric motors, transformers, vacuum tubes, television, and a host of other appliances. Many times it is a long, trying, and expensive route from the discovery of the basic principle to an acceptable application.

The engineer is interested in the ultimate application. Frequently, however, it is necessary for him to carry his research close to or actually into the basic area. There are many examples of basic discoveries made while pursuing applied research, in the same way that basic discoveries have been made while searching for quite different basic information.

In universities, work beyond the master's degree requires a thesis based upon original fundamental research. When graduate work was first being developed, it was desired that the student become progressively more independent of the teacher. Research provided the environment for this kind of instruction, progressing as it did further and further into the unknown and requiring more and more original and independent thought on the part of the student. As time has gone on, however, it has been forgotten that the reason for adoption of research was for the sake of its climate. Quite generally today, graduate work is conceived to have as its objective the *training* of a researcher.

If you intend to enter the field of research, whether pure or applied, you should plan to go through to the doctor's degree. If you wish to work in the applied field, a doctor's degree in engineering would be appropriate. If you desire, however, to work in the fundamental field of research, you should give careful thought to whether your doctorate should be in a field of science or in a branch of engineering. In either case your first degree could well be in engineering.

Engineers as Teachers

Each year there are a number of openings at various levels on faculties of engineering schools. For those who have a love of the profession and who also have an enthusiasm for teaching young men, the teaching of engineering offers great rewards. A good engineering teacher should be well fortified with sound engineering experience involving direct responsibility for worthwhile engineering achievements. At the same time he should be well prepared in the scientific support underlying the branch of engineering he is to teach. Research experience is important, but it cannot replace professional experience that responsible practice requires and provides, if the teacher is to prepare his students for engineering responsibilities rather than for research.

Women in Engineering

We have discussed the engineer and engineering as though all engineers were men and engineering a world for men. This is not strictly true, since there are a few engineers who are women. The first woman engineer in this country left college about seventy years ago. For a long time women engineers were about as rare as women physicians were, but during the past thirty years the number graduating from engineering schools has been increasing. Although that number is still not large, women engineers have had their proportionate share of distinguished practitioners.

In every branch of engineering there are professional functions that can be performed perfectly well by women. Except for some of the more rigorous jobs in construction and heavy manufacture, women could do the work as well as men. In Russia women engineers are even occupying some of these rigorous jobs. Women who have the aptitude and the inclination will find many opportunities open to them upon completion of their engineering training. There are no problems for them in engineering that do not exist for a career woman in any profession.

16
A Look Ahead

We have traced the developments wrought by the engineer from crude beginnings in ancient times to the great achievements of the present day. We have followed his development of transportation on the ground, the sea, and in the air; the evolution of communication from the wired circuit through wireless telegraph and telephone to color television, radar and radio astronomy; the development of electric power for manufacture; the development of a host of new materials, metallic, ceramic, and plastic; the development of safe water supply and sanitation; the development of machines and processes of industry; and more recently, the development of new applications of nuclear reactions. We are at present embarked upon a project that may lead to transport in outer space, possibly to the moon and back and perhaps later to other planets.

One may wonder what there is left for the engineer to do, except perhaps service this vast array of facilities. One may wonder whether there are any real frontiers left to explore except outer space.

Something under 5 percent of our scientific and engineering manpower is engaged on space projects, including the moon venture. At this stage one may question whether a trip to the moon will do more than satisfy man's curiosity. Even if valuable materials were found there, the problem of transporting them to earth would be considerable, and the likelihood of finding valuable materials seems at this stage relatively remote. The hostile environment is not conducive to prolonged habitation by man. We do not yet know whether man can endure the unchecked radiation of outer space and, hence, an occupancy of the moon. Manned space flight orbiting the earth will continue at an increasing rate; and unmanned vehicles will continue to probe the nature of deep space, the moon, and other planets.

A major product of space flight has resulted from the engineering required for operation in a new environment. New materials and new procedures have been developed. A new approach has been required, which will result in a beneficial review of many materials and procedures.

About 25 percent of our scientific and engineering manpower is engaged in defense research and development. This includes both government and industrial enterprise. Defense activities will tend to be reduced in proportion to the reasonableness of man's attitude toward man.

We thus see that over 70 percent of our scientific and engineering manpower is engaged in civilian, peacetime endeavors. These are largely directed toward finding, developing, and applying new materials, new fuels, new machines, new processes, and new systems; and the maintenance, improvement, and operation of existing facilities, processes, and products.

Are there any really new frontiers that remain to be explored? History tells us that by and large no great effort is put into exploration unless a political or economic benefit is expected, or unless there is a pressing necessity, such as the preservation of security or health. What I propose to discuss will meet these criteria. Some of the unknown regions are already being probed tentatively, but only a few subdivisions have received serious consideration or have been put under serious attack.

Let us start with solar energy. The sun pours down upon us enormous amounts of energy each day. We spend a great deal of time, effort, and money sheltering ourselves from the sun and offsetting the heat that it brings us. We have done little toward harnessing it for domestic and industrial needs.

It seems reasonable that in the major portion of our country energy from the sun may be harnessed to do many things that now require the importation of fuels from sources that are certainly not inexhaustible. We could not only heat water but we could heat and cool residences and commercial buildings. Heating homes has been attempted but only in a very primitive fashion. The energy is available if it is properly harnessed. For example, a 5-foot searchlight reflector will collect enough solar energy to melt, at 6,150°F, a rod of tungsten placed at the focal point.

The next important frontier is the ocean. I suppose man's early experiences with water and with the sea have turned him against the thought of its great benevolence. Man has been reluctant to explore the sea to the extent that he has already explored the air. Navigation in shallow depths has been undertaken by the Navy in submarines. Much of the rest of sea exploration has been done from the surface with instruments, or from a diving bell, or by divers. Only a few intrepid souls like William Beebe, Jacques Cousteau,

Jacques Piccard, and Don Walsh have made exploratory trips into the ocean depths. Piccard and Walsh have descended nearly seven miles into the world's greatest depths.

Man has turned to flights in outer space; yet more than seven-tenths of the surface of the earth is still relatively unknown to him. Exploration of the oceans can lead to tangible benefits for all people. The oceanographers have been busy in recent years mapping the surface of the ocean floor and taking samples from it for study. Naturalists have been studying marine life brought up in trawls and dredges. It is estimated that the ocean could feed the earth's population and that it contains practically all known minerals in solution. It is suspected too that large quantities of minerals exist on the ocean floor. Active exploration of our continental shelf should be undertaken.

On land there are many areas where water is unavailable, unusable, or is running short. Active development is already in progress of methods for desalting sea water so that it may be used for agriculture, industry, and human consumption. The state of development is not yet at a satisfactory economic basis. The transfer of water over long distances is likely.

It is conceivable that some day a means will be found so that man may live for a considerable time underneath the sea. This would at least be an achievement that would be impossible in outer space unless we could find a benevolent planet. Tests are being made now, but we do not yet have the answers needed for continued under-water living. Man's innate fear of the water has no doubt prevented a more active development of submarine transportation, but beneath the sea one escapes the violent turbulence of the

surface in stormy weather. With electronic devices as aids
to navigation, under-water transport should be possible.
With nuclear propelled ships, prolonged submergence is
feasible. Submarines have already transited the Arctic
Ocean under the ice cap.

Another great frontier that has not received the attention
it deserves is the application of biology to engineering
problems. We are familiar with the fact that processes have
been devised for the development in the pharmaceutical
field of the so-called wonder drugs. We are likewise familiar with the use of insecticides for the control of farm crops
and for the protection of animals and human beings. Biochemical engineers have a hand in the preparation of such
products.

An area not so well known is concerned with the effect
of microorganisms on corrosion of metals and other materials. Many paints are attacked by microorganisms. Many
microorganisms promote chemical reactions. We are familiar with the fact that fermentation processes are promoted
by microorganisms. It is known that some microorganisms
can achieve in one step a result that would require perhaps
a dozen steps in chemical reactions.

This is a very complex field. The number of species of
bacteria, spores, viruses, and other organisms is unknown,
but it is undoubtedly very large. The inter-relation of these
organisms and the biological chain of events amongst them
are likewise unknown. Where one chain of circumstances is
put under control, another undesirable chain may show up.
There is strong indication, however, that in one way or another, microorganisms will become progressively more involved in engineering processes, in their effects on engi-

neering materials and in the development of new processes and products.

Many established procedures in engineering should be reviewed and overhauled in the light of today's added knowledge. Many processes and products could be considerably improved by subjecting them to an attack employing the latest engineering knowledge and techniques. It seems to be a trait of the human mind to follow earlier acquired approaches and ways of thinking, and it is very difficult to free the mind sufficiently to try a new approach to a problem. Newcomers to a field may be a refreshing influence even if a disturbing one.

The population of the United States is now growing at such a rate that it will double in about sixty years. Thus sixty years from now the population will be about 400 million. About half of our present population lives in urban communities. It is estimated that sixty years hence about 80 percent, or over 300 million, will live in urban communities. In your professional lifetime, therefore, you will see the urban population treble.

It is not clear what part of the country will be subjected most to such an enormous urban gain. During the 1950s Southern California gained over 50 percent in population and the southwestern states gained about 40 percent. Some states have not kept up with the national rate of increase.

Water supply, transportation needs (both rail and highway), and power for both domestic and industrial uses must be developed. In order to prepare for such a population increase, planning on a large scale will be required of all branches of engineering working in cooperation with their fellow professionals, the architects. Regional planning will take on a more important meaning than in the past, and in many cases existing facilities will need revision or rearrangement.

Such planning cannot be done on the basis of technical considerations alone. Economic and social considerations will usually predominate among influences causing migration. In turn, the planning of urban areas must provide for social, economic, and cultural activities within the region. Regional and urban planning become an immediate frontier for engineers now entering the profession.

There are *many* frontiers to be explored, and there are exciting new fields to challenge engineers for a long time to come. The number of problems is increasing, they are becoming more complex, and some of them, at least, are becoming more urgent. The means for attacking these new problems are increasing and improving constantly. Surely there was never a time when engineers faced greater challenge and opportunity.

Appendix

ECPD *Canons of Ethics of Engineers* *

FUNDAMENTAL PRINCIPLES OF PROFESSIONAL ENGINEERING
ETHICS

The Engineer, to uphold and advance the honor and dignity
of the engineering profession and in keeping with high standards of ethical conduct:

   I. Will be honest and impartial, and will serve with devo-
     tion his employer, his clients, and the public;

  II. Will strive to increase the competence and prestige of
     the engineering profession;

III. Will use his knowledge and skill for the advancement
     of human welfare.

RELATIONS WITH THE PUBLIC

1.1. The Engineer will have proper regard for the safety,
health, and welfare of the public in the performance of his
professional duties.

1.2. He will endeavor to extend public knowledge and
appreciation of engineering and its achievements, and will
oppose any untrue, unsupported, or exaggerated statements
regarding engineering.

* Approved by Engineers' Council for Professional Development,
September 30, 1963.

1.3. He will be dignified and modest in explaining his work and merit, will ever uphold the honor and dignity of his profession, and will refrain from self-laudatory advertising.

1.4. He will express an opinion on an engineering subject only when it is founded on adequate knowledge and honest conviction.

1.5. He will preface any *ex parte* statements, criticisms, or arguments that he may issue by clearly indicating on whose behalf they are made.

RELATIONS WITH EMPLOYERS AND CLIENTS

2.1. The Engineer will act in professional matters as a faithful agent or trustee for each employer or client.

2.2. He will act fairly and justly toward vendors and contractors, and will not accept from vendors or contractors, any commissions or allowances, directly or indirectly.

2.3. He will inform his employer or client if he is financially interested in any vendor or contractor, or in any invention, machine, or apparatus, which is involved in a project or work of his employer or client. He will not allow such interest to affect his decisions regarding engineering services which he may be called upon to perform.

2.4. He will indicate to his employer or client the adverse consequences to be expected if his engineering judgment is overruled.

2.5. He will undertake only those engineering assignments for which he is qualified. He will engage or advise his employer or client to engage specialists and will cooperate with them whenever his employer's or client's interests are served best by such an arrangement.

2.6. He will not disclose information concerning the business affairs or technical processes of any present or former employer or client without his consent.

2.7. He will not accept compensation—financial or otherwise—from more than one party for the same service, or for other services pertaining to the same work, without the consent of all interested parties.

2.8. The employed engineer will engage in supplementary employment or consulting practice only with the consent of his employer.

RELATIONS WITH ENGINEERS

3.1. The Engineer will take care that credit for engineering work is given to those to whom credit is properly due.

3.2. He will provide a prospective engineering employee with complete information on working conditions and his proposed status of employment, and after employment will keep him informed of any changes in them.

3.3. He will uphold the principle of appropriate and adequate compensation for those engaged in engineering work, including those in subordinate capacities.

3.4. He will endeavor to provide opportunity for the professional development and advancement of engineers in his employ or under his supervision.

3.5. He will not injure maliciously the professional reputation, prospects, or practice of another engineer. However, if he has proof that another engineer has been unethical, illegal, or unfair in his practice, he should so advise the proper authority.

3.6. He will not compete unfairly with another engineer.

3.7. He will not invite or submit price proposals for professional services, which require creative intellectual effort, on a basis that constitutes competition on price alone. Due regard should be given to all professional aspects of the engagement.

3.8. He will cooperate in advancing the engineering profession by interchanging information and experience with other engineers and students, and by contributing to public communication media, to the efforts of engineering and scientific societies and schools.